Never Mind the

the

BULLOCKS

HERE'S the SCIENCE

Dr Karl Kruszelnicki

Illustrated by Adam Yazxhi

HarperCollinsPublishers

HarperCollins*Publishers*

First published in Australia in 2009
by HarperCollins*Publishers* Australia Pty Limited
ABN 36 009 913 517
harpercollins.com.au

Copyright © Karl S. Kruszelnicki Pty Ltd 2009
Illustrations and cover design copyright © Maxco Creative Media 2009

The right of Karl Kruszelnicki and Adam Yazxhi to be identified as the
author and illustrator of this work has been asserted by them in accordance with
the *Copyright Amendment (Moral Rights) Act 2000*.

HarperCollins*Publishers*
25 Ryde Road, Pymble, Sydney, NSW 2073, Australia
31 View Road, Glenfield, Auckland 0627, New Zealand
A 53, Sector 57, Noida, UP, India
77–85 Fulham Palace Road, London, W6 8JB, United Kingdom
2 Bloor Street East, 20th floor, Toronto, Ontario M4W 1A8, Canada
10 East 53rd Street, New York NY 10022, USA

National Library of Australia Cataloguing-in-Publication data:

Kruszelnicki, Karl, 1948– .
 Never mind the bullocks, here's the science / Dr Karl Kruszelnicki.
 ISBN: 978 0 7322 8537 1 (pbk.)
 Bibliography.
 1. Science – Popular works.
500

Cover photography: Jo Duck
Cover design and internal illustrations: Adam Yazxhi / MAXCO creative
Additional illustrations: 'NASA astronaut' on p 8 by Max Yazxhi (aged 6½);
    'Velcro loops and hooks' on p 6 by Zac Yazxhi (aged 3½); additional illustrations on
    pp 4 and 8 by students from KJP Kindergarten Class, Avalon Public School, NSW
Typesett in Minion 11.5/17pt by Letter Spaced
Printed and bound in Australia by Griffin Press
70gsm Classic White used by HarperCollins*Publishers* is a natural, recyclable product made
from wood grown in sustainable forests. The manufacturing processes conform to the
environmental regulations in the country of origin, Finland.

6 5 4 3 2 1   09 10 11 12

Contents

Velcro and NASA

(A Ripping Yarn)

In 1957, the Soviet Union successfully launched the first artificial satellite, the *Sputnik*. This scared the heck out of the United States. So, in 1958, in response to the perceived threat posed by the Soviet Space Program, the US President Dwight D. Eisenhower set up the National Aeronautics and Space Administration (NASA). NASA was given a mandate to 'pioneer the future in space exploration, scientific discovery and aeronautics research' — to boldly go you-know-where.

NASA Does Everything ...

NASA was extraordinarily successful. NASA got us to the Moon and sent successful probes to most of the planets in the solar system. It pioneered the use of spacecraft to look back at our little Blue Planet, and to make very precise and useful long-term measurements.

But NASA also did lots of non-space-related, space-age research. These spin-offs include cordless vacuum cleaners, space-age lubricants, programmable heart pacemakers, heated goggles, unsinkable life rafts, fireproof fabrics and foam, and even VHT TrackBite, a heat-resistant gloop that is laid on racetracks to provide better grip for the tyres.

In 2008, NASA had their well-deserved 50th anniversary celebrations. In all the hype of the celebrations, various news media trotted out the claim that 'NASA invented Velcro'. Velcro™ is that hook-and-loop, two-sided fabric fastener which pulls apart with a distinctive ripping sound.

Aliens Invented Velcro?

In the 1996 movie *The Island of Dr Moreau*, it is mentioned that Dr Moreau received the Nobel Prize for inventing Velcro. In the 1997 movie *Men in Black*, K mentions in passing that Velcro was an alien invention. And in the 2002 'Carbon Creek' episode of *Star Trek Enterprise*, Velcro was supposedly given to Earthlings by Vulcans who crash-landed here in 1957.

... Except Velcro

NASA has contributed to the invention of many things, but Velcro is not one of them.

Nope, Velcro was invented by the Swiss aristocrat (and engineer, or maybe mountaineer) Georges de Mestral, who was born in 1907. (I should point out that his story has been retold so many times that it suffers from the Chinese Whispers Syndrome, and so many of the details have changed in the retelling. For example, his name is given as George/Georges DeMestral/de Mestral/de Mertral, depending on your references. However, I have used the version that I believe is the most credible.) Georges was a gifted child, obtaining his first patent at the age of 12, for a model aeroplane.

In 1941 (or 1948, or the early 1950s, depending on whom you read) he went for a walk in the Alps (or the local woods) with his

Irish Pointer (or sometimes, by himself). It was the mating season for the burdock — a large herb-type plant belonging to the daisy family. After the burdock is fertilised, its hook-bearing flowers turn into woody burrs (also called 'cockleburs'). These woody burrs are perfectly evolved to cling to passing animals or birds, so that the seeds can be widely dispersed. After Georges returned from his walk, he noticed that his trouser legs — and his dog's coat — were covered with these burdock burrs.

The 'Aha' Moment

Instead of getting annoyed, he got scientific and examined the burrs under his microscope (yes, every home should have one). He saw that each burr had a myriad of tiny hooks. It was these hooks that had fastened onto the loops of thread in his clothes, and the loops of the coiled hairs in his dog's coat.

He then realised that, potentially, this was a really neat way to fasten clothes. But it took him eight years of research and experimentation to develop this simple idea into a commercial product.

He needed a set of fabric 'hooks' that would stick to a set of fabric 'loops'. So he collaborated with a weaver (or professor) in

Vel-Cro, the Name

Georges de Mestral first called it 'locking tape'. The name Velcro came later. Even though it was first made from nylon, 'nylon' is not incorporated into its name.

Velcro is derived from the first syllables of two French words – *velours* (meaning 'velvet', chosen purely because de Mestral liked the sound of the word) and *crochet* (meaning 'hook').

HOw It ALL BeGAn

Velcro was invented by the Swiss aristocrat (and engineer, or mountaineer) Georges de Mestral, who was born in 1907.

HIS DOG

GEORGES DE MESTRAL

(both drawn through the eyes of a kindergarten student)

the sIMPLIFIed story

Circa 1941, Georges took his dog for a walk in the Alps (or the local woods). It was the mating season for the burdock – a large herb-type plant, which belongs to the daisy family. After the burdock is fertilised, its hook-bearing flowers turn into woody burrs (also called 'cockleburs'). These burrs are perfectly suited to clinging to passing animals, birds, or even Georges and his dog, so that the seeds can be widely dispersed.

BURDOCK

Lyon in France to make them. In one early breakthrough they realised that they could make 'hooks' by cutting the 'loops' in half. Together they managed to make strips of cotton fabric that had tiny hooks on one strip of fabric and, on the other, matching tiny loops for the hooks to grip onto. The two strips of fabric stuck together, but only for a short time. The grip between the hoops and the loops rapidly weakened with repeated use, because the cotton fabric was too weak and the hooks began to break in increasing numbers.

His research led him to test fabric strips of plain nylon, then thicker nylon, and then nylon with added polyester. He finally got the Velcro mix right with a nylon/polyester combination strengthened by heat-treating it under infrared lamps. By the mid-1950s (or 1951) de Mestral's first patents for Velcro were granted, and he began to branch out overseas. By the late 1950s, his invention was being praised in US newspapers as the 'Zipperless Zipper'. A lot of Velcro was being made — about 60,000 km in the late 1950s.

Velcro Pluses and Minuses

The tearing noise that Velcro makes as it unpeels can be a plus (to warn that a pickpocket is trying to steal your wallet) or a minus (a soldier trying to move silently in enemy territory). There is a military version of Velcro that is 95% less noisy, but the details of its manufacture are classified.

On the minus side, Velcro can stick to some fabrics, and its hooks can gather unwanted fur, dust and hair. But on the plus side you can use this 'accumulation' property to remove tissue paper, cloth pile balls and dog hair from clothing.

HOOKed up in the Loops

It took Georges de Mestral eight years of research and experimentation to develop this simple idea into a commercial product. He needed 'hooks' that would stick to 'loops'.

THE LOOPS

 Georges realised that the hooks of the burrs had fastened onto the loops of thread in his clothes, and the loops of the coiled hairs in his dog's coat. This revelation formed the idea of Velcro for Georges.

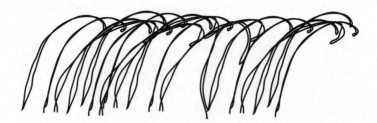

THE HOOKS

Function, Not Art

Unfortunately, while de Mestral's early Velcro was very functional, it did not look very fashionable. He had originally hoped that his Velcro would be used everywhere — in suits to replace buttons, in shoes to replace laces, and so on. But this did not happen, because while Velcro attracted the reputation of being useful, it was lacking in style. This hindered its acceptance into the world of fashion.

But in the weightless world of Outer Space, it was a different story. Velcro got its first major public exposure in NASA's Space Program. Velcro was used to attach food pouches to walls, notepads to astronauts' legs, and even to attach astronauts' bodies to the spaceship wall for sleeping. Indeed, each space shuttle uses about a quarter of a kilometre of Velcro. It's even stuck inside astronauts' helmets, so that they can tilt their heads to scratch their noses against it.

That's how NASA became linked to Velcro — *not* because NASA invented it.

And ever since NASA and Velcro got stuck together, nobody's been able to tear them apart.

Wall-Jumping

The rather odd 'sport' of 'Velcro wall-jumping' involves running at a wall (sometimes bouncing off a trampoline) with the aim of attaching oneself as high on the wall as possible.

David Letterman made this 'sport' famous by performing it on *Late Night with David Letterman* on 28 February 1984.

LAunchiNG MAKes MG Itchy

Each space shuttle uses about a quarter of a kilometre of Velcro. But even before 1981, NASA was linked to Velcro – and not because NASA invented it.

Velcro is even stuck inside our helmets, so we can tilt our heads to scratch our noses against it.

NASA ASTRONAUT
(as seen by a six-year-old)

Cars and Spaceships

The first Velcro was made from cotton fabric. Because this material was too weak, it was replaced by nylon, with polyester sometimes added.

The Velcro used on the space shuttle is made with Teflon for the loops, polyester for the hooks, and the backing is made from a type of glass. In the UK, the Warwick Manufacturing Group is developing hooks and loops that are tiny – of the order of nanometres, or billionths of a metre. Car makers, including Jaguar, are interested in using the group's idea to assemble cars.

References

Binney, Ruth (Editor), *The Origins of Everyday Things*, London: Reader's Digest, 1998, p 130.

Freeman, Allyn and Golden, Bob, *Why Didn't I think of That: Bizarre Origins of Ingenious Inventions We Couldn't Live Without*, New York: John Wiley & Sons, Inc., 1997, pp 99–101.

'NASA spinoffs: fact or myth', *Invention & Technology*, Fall 2008, Vol 23, Issue 3, pp 38, 39.

Panati, Charles, *Extraordinary Origins of Everyday Things*, New York: Harper & Row, 1987, pp 317, 318.

Roberts, Royston M., *Serendipity: Accidental Discoveries in Science*, New York: John Wiley & Sons, Inc., 1989, pp 220–222.

Schwarcz, Dr Joe, *Dr. Joe & What You Didn't Know: 177 Fascinating Questions & Answers About the Chemistry of Everyday Life*, Toronto, Ont: ECW Press, 2003, pp 178, 179.

WAter-powered Car

(This Car is Hydromatic)

Once you get a bunch of hot-rod motor-heads together, sooner or later the talk will turn to the 'invention' of the 'Car Powered By Tap Water'. This Big Conspiracy story always involves Big Business and/or Big Government. Apparently, in the recent (or distant) past, a poorly defined consortium of evil politicians and/or car manufacturers and/or oil companies suppressed this marvellous invention (i.e. a water-powered car) to protect their own interests. Even Conspiracy Theorists who don't drive cars believe this myth.

It's an attractive myth because it's so simple. There are a few different versions.

1 — Very Simple, Burn Water

The first version of this myth is incredibly simple. The story is that all you have to do is make some cheap modifications to your engine, or carburettor, or fuel injection system. You can then run your Internal Combustion Engine by pouring water (not petrol) into the fuel tank.

However, there's a very simple and fundamental reason why you cannot power a car by burning water in the engine. And that is because the water has already been burnt, and so the chemical energy has been used up!

Let me explain.

When you burn coal in a furnace, the chemical reaction gives you carbon dioxide and heat. After the fire is out, some ashes remain. These ashes are the leftovers from burning the coal.

You cannot burn those ashes again — they have already been burnt.

Water is Burnt Ashes

The situation is the same for water — i.e. the water has already been burnt.

When you burn hydrogen and oxygen in a chemical reaction, you get water and heat. When each NASA space shuttle thunders upwards into Space, its external tank carries about 617 tonnes of liquid oxygen and about 103 tonnes of liquid hydrogen. They are burnt together to produce about 720 tonnes of water — which is instantaneously turned into steam by the heat of the chemical reaction. This steam builds up inside the rocket engine with enormous pressure, and is released through the nozzles of the rocket engine. These nozzles point down to the ground. And so, thanks to the rule 'for every Action there is an equal and opposite Reaction', the space shuttle is pushed upwards — 'to infinity and beyond'.

After the steam comes out of the space shuttle rocket nozzles, it cools down. The gaseous steam turns into droplets of liquid water, which appear as a long skinny vertical cloud behind the rising space shuttle.

So when you start with hydrogen and oxygen, you can combine them to give you water and heat. Water might be 'wet' like petrol, but it has also been burnt, like coal ashes.

Think of water merely as wet ashes. It has already been burnt, so it can't be burnt again (just like coal ashes — they have been

WhO Put wAt@r In MY P@troL tANK?

FUEL
(FILL WITH WATER ONLY)

A good conspiracy story always involves Big Business and/or
Big Government. One great plot revolves around a poorly defined
consortium of evil politicians and/or car manufacturers and/or
oil companies who suppressed this marvellous invention
(of a water-powered car) to protect their own interests.

THE FUEL OF THE FUTURE?

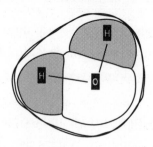

No biggy ... just a good ol' water molecule (H_2O)

burnt and can't be burnt again). So you can't get any more chemical energy out of the water, because the energy has already been released.

2 — Pretty Simple, Burn Hydrogen

There is a roundabout way of producing energy out of this wet liquid water — and that's the background to *another* version of the Run-Your-Car-On-Water myth. If you split the water back into its components, which are oxygen and hydrogen, you can burn them.

Scientists have been doing this for centuries. It's so simple that you can build the mechanism in your workshop and install it in your car.

Pour the water into a tank that has a metal electrode at each end, and then shove some electricity into those electrodes. The energy in the electricity will split the liquid water (H_2O) into bubbles of hydrogen gas at one electrode and bubbles of oxygen gas at the other electrode.

Then there are two choices.

One is to run the engine entirely on hydrogen by burning it in the cylinders instead of burning petrol. It can be done, but it requires a lot of tinkering with the computers that run the engine.

The other choice is much more popular. As usual, fill the tank with petrol, and let it run the engine. But use the electricity from the alternator to split water into hydrogen and oxygen, and then pipe the hydrogen — and sometimes the oxygen — gas into the air filter of your engine, from where it gets sucked in and burnt. This will supposedly increase your fuel economy by up to 300%. But could this really work?

TANSTAAFL

Well, it is true that electricity will split water into hydrogen and oxygen, which can be burnt in the engine.

But the Laws of Thermodynamics stop you from getting energy for nothing. (By the way, the casual or layman's form of the Three Laws of Thermodynamics are (1) you cannot win, (2) you cannot break even and (3) you will always lose.)

Yes, you can get energy from the hydrogen and oxygen, produced by splitting water with electricity — but you have to put more energy in than you get out. For example, if you put in 100 units of energy to split the water into hydrogen and oxygen, you will get back only (say) 80 units of energy when you recombine the hydrogen and oxygen.

Robert Heinlein popularised the Three Laws of Thermodynamics in his 1966 novel *The Moon is a Harsh Mistress*. He summed them up in one neat acronym: TANSTAAFL — which stands for 'There Ain't No Such Thing As A Free Lunch'. You won't get more energy back than you put in, and thanks to losses (e.g. friction and heat), you will always get less. So, sadly, you can't increase fuel economy by 300% just by adding hydrogen into a petrol-burning engine.

3 — Myths Galore

Luckily for the Conspiracy Theorists, there are other sources of energy besides chemical energy upon which to base new myths. These include gravitational energy, kinetic energy, heat energy, electrical energy, magnetic energy and nuclear energy. However, nobody has yet succeeded in using any of these kinds of energy with water to propel a car with an Internal Combustion Engine. So perhaps it's time to hose down such far-fetched ideas.

Combustion, Internal or External?

Why do people talk about the Internal Combustion Engine? Is there an External Combustion Engine?

Yes. Both the Internal and the External Combustion Engines generate work by pushing pistons inside a cylinder. And, in each case, pistons move because the gas (the working fluid) inside the cylinder is at a high pressure.

But in an External Combustion Engine, the gas is generated by having the burning happen outside the engine. The advantage is that it makes the burning very clean and efficient. However, there is a disadvantage – the extra weight of a separate combustion chamber. So, in a steam engine, the fire happens inside the boiler turning water into steam, and the steam is then piped to another location where the cylinders are.

In an Internal Combustion Engine, the burning happens inside the engine, where the moving parts are. In a jet engine the kerosene is burnt inside the engine – and the same goes for a rocket engine. And yes, the petrol is burnt inside the Internal Combustion Engine of an automobile. The advantage is the reduction in weight – but the disadvantage lies in trying to get a clean burn. Car engines were always 'dirty', until computers cleaned them up, by constantly monitoring and adjusting the burn cycle.

References

Allen, Mike, 'The truth about water-powered cars: mechanic's diary', *Popular Mechanics*, 3 July 2008.

Allen, Mike, 'Water-powered cars: hydrogen electrolyzer mod can't up MPGs', *Popular Mechanics*, 7 August 2008.

BrAKe Assist

(PAdding the FACts)

Let me tell you the sad story of a friend of mine who smashed her car into the car in front of her. (Happily, nobody got hurt.)

Unfortunately, she wrongly believed that hitting the brakes as hard as possible was very dangerous.

O Woe is She

In all her years of driving, she had never once braked flat out. On this occasion, she was adjusting her car radio in heavy traffic and had taken her eyes off the road to find the tuning knob. (It's never a good idea to take your eyes off the road while driving.) When she looked up from the radio, to her overwhelming horror, she saw that she was about to smash into the back of the car in front of her. The car in front had slowed dramatically, without her noticing (because she was looking at the radio not the road).

If she had hit the brakes hard, she might have avoided the crash.

But her driving skills had become rusty over the years, and she had never done an Advanced Driving Course. For some unknown reason, she believed that if she planted her foot as hard as she could on the brake pedal, the car would skid out of control.

And so, with the car in front rapidly looming larger in her

windscreen, she pressed carefully on the brake pedal and, in perfect control, smashed into the car in front. The damage to both cars cost many thousands of dollars to repair and probably wouldn't have happened if she had hit the brake pedal hard enough.

But she isn't alone in thinking this way.

History of Cars and Brakes

In 1885, Gottlieb Daimler built a petrol Internal Combustion Engine motorbike (just a wooden pushbike with a motor), and Carl Benz built a petrol Internal Combustion Engine three-wheeler car (which had a top speed of about 13 kph). The next year, Daimler fitted his engine to a horse carriage, thus creating the world's first four-wheeled car.

The first car brakes were modified bicycle brakes, activated by steel wires. In 1902, Louis Renault invented the drum brake. In a drum brake, a brake shoe covered with friction material pushes against the inside of a drum, fixed to the road wheel. The friction material, being inside the sealed drum, is not in the moving air. This means that the friction material cannot readily get rid of any heat that it may generate. Indeed, after repeated braking — e.g. coming down a steep hill with a big load — the friction material can get very hot and lose its friction. This loss of ability to slow down is called 'brake fade'.

In 1908, Henry Ford began large-scale mass production of the car. The price plummeted, making cars more affordable. The first all-steel body was built in 1914.

At the time, car brakes were activated by steel wires which needed very careful adjustment to make them pull equally on each wheel. In 1921, hydraulic brakes were invented. They automatically applied equal pressure to each wheel brake. By the late 1920s, brakes on all four wheels were becoming popular.

In the 1960s, disc brakes — with their greater resistance to brake fade — became more common in motor vehicles. In disc brakes, friction material is squeezed against a rotating disc, fixed to the road wheel. Because both the friction material and the disc are in the moving air, they can more readily get rid of their heat. Nevertheless, after very severe repeated braking, even disc brakes can fade.

Friction Ain't Friction

It turns out that when a car brakes hard, there are two types of friction involved — 'Static' and 'Dynamic'. And Static Friction is not as great as Dynamic Friction.

Imagine this scenario: you brake as hard as you can, planting your foot on the brake pedal with all your force. All the brakes work well, grabbing the road wheels so firmly that they come to a complete halt. This is called 'locking the brakes' or 'locking the tyres'. Your car slides down the road, slowing fairly rapidly, with a small patch of rubber on each wheel being your only contact with the road. These four patches of rubber get very hot, and rubber smoke gusts into the air as strips of rubber leave the tyres and melt into the road. This is accompanied by a loud screeching noise.

It's all very satisfying, but there are two problems with this scenario.

First, while each patch of rubber was getting very hot as the stationary tyre skidded down the road, you lost all steering ability. You could turn the steering wheel either way, but it would make no difference to where the car went. Therefore, if your car was aimed slightly off the road when you locked the brakes, you would veer off the road in that direction — for as long as your brakes were locked. Of course, you could take your foot off the brakes and regain steering control — but you would no longer be slowing down.

Second, you were not stopping as quickly as you possibly could. The Static Friction (when your tyre is static, and no longer rotating) is not as great as Dynamic Friction (where the tyre is not locked, but still grabbing the road).

What to do?

Anti-Lock Braking System (ABS)

Well, if you were a professional racing or rally driver, you'd know what to do. You would apply the maximum amount of pressure on the brake pedal that would almost (but not quite) lock the brakes. And if you felt the brakes lock, you would back off the pressure, and then re-apply it. But the vast majority of drivers are not skilled enough to do this.

Back in 1929, French aircraft and automobile enthusiast Gabriel Voison invented an Anti-lock Braking System (ABS) for aircraft. It first appeared in cars in the 1966 Jensen Interceptor FF. And Mercedes-Benz introduced the first fully electronic four-wheel ABS system in 1987. Today, practically all new cars have ABS — and if a car you'd like to buy doesn't have ABS, don't buy it!

ABS relies on your hitting the brakes as hard as you can. Then it monitors each of the four wheels. The moment that one wheel begins to rotate a lot slower than the other wheels (and is about to lock up), the ABS drops the hydraulic pressure to just that wheel. It then re-applies the pressure. Modern ABS can do this 20 times per second. What you, the driver, feels is the brake pedal 'pulsating' or vibrating under your foot. This is a little disconcerting at first but is entirely normal.

With ABS, not only can you stop in the minimum distance, but you can also steer the car in any direction you aim it. I love ABS.

*i CAN't st*o*p*
*th*I*s F*e*e*L*INC*

When there is a sudden lifting of the foot off the accelerator pedal,
AND a sudden shift of the foot from the accelerator to the brake pedal,
BUT the driver has not applied vigorous pressure, THEN the
Brake Assist system takes over and applies full braking power.
It somehow 'recognises' that a panic stop is needed,
and takes control.

During emergency braking, the Anti-lock Braking System (quite different
from Brake Assist, but you have to have it for Brake Assist to work)
prevents any risk of wheel locking and thus
helps you better control any loss of grip
(i.e. you can both steer and brake at the same time).

In Australia, in 2003, the Monash University Accident Research Centre discovered that ABS reduced the number of multiple-vehicle crashes by 18%, and the number of crashes where the car ran off the road by 35%.

But drivers still have to know how to use their brakes properly.

Brake Assist

Even back in the 1990s, a few car manufacturers were well aware of this gap in the education of many drivers. In 1992, Mercedes-Benz tested drivers in a simulated emergency braking situation. The results proved to be very interesting.

The act of braking has two parts — first, shifting your foot onto the brake pedal and, second, applying pressure. In the Mercedes-Benz study there was no real problem with the first part. In an emergency situation, about three-quarters of drivers tested would shift their right foot very quickly from the accelerator to the brake pedal. The problem occurred with the second part. Over 90% of drivers simply would not press the brake pedal hard enough to achieve maximum braking.

It seemed that, deep down, many drivers believed the myth that heavy braking makes you lose control of your car.

For this reason, Mercedes-Benz (and others) began to develop a system that they called 'Brake Assist'. Mercedes-Benz introduced it in 1996 and, to their credit, made it standard on all of their cars by 1998. BMW and Volvo followed soon after. There are moves in Europe to make Brake Assist compulsory on all new cars sold in the European Union.

So how does Brake Assist work?

When there is a sudden lifting of the foot off the accelerator pedal, followed by a sudden shift of the foot from the accelerator to the brake pedal, and the driver has not applied vigorous pressure, then the Brake Assist system takes over and applies full braking power. It somehow 'recognises' that a panic stop is needed and takes over.

Of course, the system takes into account your road speed, as well as other conditions. It is clever enough not to activate when the driver is an enthusiast or racing driver doing heavy braking as they enter a tight corner at high speed. So enthusiasts would still have fine control of their braking.

However, the average driver is not so skilful. Typically, the average person can get a car to come to a complete stop from 100 kph in about 73 m — but Brake Assist can reduce this to about 40 m. Today, many manufacturers (including Toyota, Nissan, Ford and Audi) have begun to introduce this kind of technology into their vehicles and one day soon it may be standard on all cars, worldwide.

Practise Panic Stops

Ever since I got my licence, I have been a car enthusiast (as opposed to somebody who just uses a car to get from A to B). About once a year, I will drive to a deserted road and practise doing a panic stop, so that the muscles of my right leg don't lose the muscle memory of what an emergency stop feels like, and (just as importantly) so that my brain knows how the car will behave (e.g. pull to the left or the right). I practise a few such stops, starting at low speeds and gradually working my way up to around the speed limit. I also taught this skill to my kids when they were learning to drive.

Most drivers will never experience a panic stop in their entire driving career — unless the Brake Assist system turns it on for them. You need to practise braking hard while you're still alive, to avoid bringing your driving career to a dead stop ...

Safety and Cost

There are two different philosophies regarding safety features in cars.

One philosophy is that you get the extra safety features only if you pay extra. This is what happened to me when I changed over from a large seven-seat car to a smaller five-seat car. In a collision, having extra mass helps you survive. In the smaller car, we no longer had the extra mass. The 'equaliser', in this case, was the safety feature of lots of airbags. Unfortunately, the only way we could get lots of airbags was to get the luxury model with dead cow and dead tree (which we didn't particularly want), reversing camera (handy, but we could live without it), Satellite Navigation (handy, but not a necessity) and the additional airbags (essential).

The other philosophy is to maximise safety. In other words, all new cars (even the cheapest) should be equipped with all the latest safety features.

I think the latter should be the *only* option.

Absinthe's murky Past

I remember the incident with brilliant clarity — or at least I think I remember it, bearing in mind the fallibility of memory. I was a first-year university student studying physics and hanging out in Wollongong's only coffee bar (at that time). The subject of absinthe, the dazzling green alcoholic drink with the very murky past, came up in conversation. I declared that it was the 'wormwood oil' in absinthe that drove its adherents mad.

How easy it is to be both confident and wrong. It seems that the wormwood oil was innocent. The culprit was the very high level of alcohol that was needed to keep the wormwood oil dissolved and the emerald-green liquid crystal clear.

Absinthe History

Absinthe was often called the 'Green Fairy', because of its colour. It was very popular with Parisian artists, poets and intellectuals of the late 19th and early 20th century. Absinthe was thought to stimulate the creative juices in a special way that alcohol did not. However, it exacted a hefty price — a disease associated with absinthe, called 'absinthism', which involved terrifying hallucinations, enfeeblement, epileptic attacks and insanity. The attacks of 'absinthism' seemed to be very different from the ones associated with alcohol, and were blamed on wormwood oil.

Wormwood is a small shrub belonging to the daisy family. Its essential oil has been used medicinally for thousands of years — against intestinal worms, for labour pains, and for liver and gall-bladder complaints. In medieval times, wormwood oil was used in alcoholic drinks in the Val-de-Travers region of western Switzerland.

In 1797, a Major Dubied and his son-in-law, Henry-Louis Pernod, opened the first absinthe distillery in the Val-de-Travers region. Absinthe's popularity spread quickly, and in 1805 Pernod opened another factory over the border in Pontarlier, France.

Absinthe was widely used by French troops in the Algerian conflicts of the 1830s and 1840s, because of its effectiveness as a tonic and an antimalarial medication. It was also thought 'that it is an agreeable bitter, that it gives an appetite, and that it gives tone to weak digestions'. The troops brought their love of absinthe back home to France with them.

In France, by the 1870s, 5 pm was *l'heure verte* (the 'green hour') when people gathered in bars to drink absinthe. Various rituals and ceremonies became associated with the preparation of the absinthe. Spoons were made with special slots to allow the absinthe to drain through a sugar cube sitting in the spoon. (The sugar counteracted the bitter taste of the absinthe.) Occasionally the absinthe-soaked sugar cube was ignited, with much ceremony. And adding water to the absinthe could lead to a magical clouding of the previously clear drink.

Absinthe had a following among the Bohemian artists of Paris. The famous 1875–76 Degas painting *Dans un Café* has the subtitle *L'Absinthe*. Apparently it was 'hissed at' when it was auctioned in the early 1890s, due to its 'depraved' subject matter. Manet painted *The Absinthe Drinker*, while in 1887 Henri de Toulouse-Lautrec did a pastel drawing of Vincent van Gogh with a glass of absinthe, while van Gogh himself painted a still life of a carafe and a glass of

The Green Fairy

Absinthe was often referred to
as the 'Green Fairy'
because of the drink's colour.

A key ingredient of absinthe is `WORMWOOD`,
a small shrub belonging to the daisy family.

absinthe. On 27 July 1890, van Gogh shot himself. A thuja tree (a source of wormwood oil) was planted on his grave, probably inspired by van Gogh's love of thuja trees, whose flame-like images he included in some of his paintings.

However, as imbibing absinthe became all the rage with Parisians, 'absinthism' also became recognised as a medical illness.

Absinthism

In 1879, a Dr Richardson wrote in *The New York Times* a fairly typical description of 'absinthism': 'The bitterness increases the craving or desire, and the confirmed habitué is soon unable to take food until he is duly primed for it by the deadly provocative. The sufferer ... is left cold, tremulous, unsteady of movement, and nauseated ... In the worst cases, the person becomes a confirmed epileptic.'

An 1882 report from *The New York Times* noted: 'The poor wretches given up to absinthe-drinking suffer from a peculiar train of nervous symptoms, the most prominent of which is epilepsy of a remarkably severe character, terminating in softening of the brain and death.' The report then discusses a man known to drink large quantities of absinthe. 'The convulsions lasted until death — four days and four nights. During the last five or six hours of life the skin of the face became almost black.'

And, of course, lurid prose was written to deter still-innocent potential imbibers from even thinking of drinking absinthe.

A typical example from *The New York Times* of 1884 had the enticing title of 'The charms of absinthe: The allurements it holds out to its victims, and the sting that comes afterwards, confessions of a Frenchman who succumbed to it'. In a bar, a disgustingly healthy and fresh-faced American youth sees a 'tall, sallow-faced Frenchman, with a heavy and carefully waxed moustache' drinking a glass of absinthe. The Frenchman tells the sorry tale of his downfall, from being a brilliant, wealthy and well-connected medical student with a glowing future, to the unwell absinthe-addicted loner who had lost his friends and his future. He confesses, '... I lost my power of reasoning. I had no more idea of a correct syllogism than I had of the man in the moon. This was followed by utter prostration. It ended in delirium tremens. I just escaped a lunatic asylum.' In response to this precautionary tale, the shaken young American vows to abstain from the awful absinthe.

And It Gets Worse ...

Despite this bad press, the consumption of absinthe increased even further in the 1880s and 1890s, especially in France.

This was due to two factors. First, an imported American bug, the aphid, had attacked French grapevines, destroying many French vineyards, and so the production of wine dropped precipitously. Second, there was a huge increase in the mass production of absinthe, significantly dropping its price. As a result, the annual consumption of absinthe in France increased by 15 times from 1875 to 1913, to some 40 million litres.

Death of French Vineyards

In the 16th century, French colonists brought European grapevines to Florida in the USA to grow grapes. They failed.

A tiny North American insect (the 'yellow aphid' or 'plant louse') attacked the roots of the European grapevines. It stabbed the roots with its snout or proboscis. It would inject toxic saliva through one 'pipe' in the proboscis and suck up the sap to feed itself through another pipe. As the plant got sick, its internal pressure reduced, making the sap too hard for the aphid to extract, so it moved to another plant. When the colonists pulled up the dead plants to examine the roots, there were no aphids – so they never realised that the aphids were the cause.

The aphids behaved quite differently on North American vines. In these native plants, they attacked the leaves, making little 'galls' on the plants – structures that were their homes, as well as nurseries to the millions of tiny baby aphids. In eight months, a single female could produce some 25 billion descendants.

Around 1860, the aphids travelled on the roots of some North American vines to Europe. They survived the trip because the new steamships were a lot faster than sailing ships. The disease first surfaced in 1863. It took three years to act. In the first year the leaves died; in the second year the grapes died and dropped off; and in the third year the vine itself died. In the otherwise very good vintage year of 1865, vines began dying in the communes of Gard and Vaucluse, for no apparent reason. In 1868, the botanist Professor Jules-Emile Planchon dug up and examined the roots of a variety of vines – i.e. healthy, dying and dead ones. He noticed the tiny yellow aphids on the healthy and dying plants, but not on the dead ones. He called this particular aphid *Phylloxera* (Greek for 'dry leaves') *vastrix* (Latin for 'devastator').

In 1870, France and Prussia went to war. France took six years to recover from this war, but it took a generation to restore the damage done to the vineyards by the aphids. In fact, aphids cost France five billion francs – twice the amount that France had to pay as reparations for its defeat by Prussia in the Franco–Prussian war.

The cure was related to the cause. The aphids did not attack North American grapevine roots. But the French did not like the taste of North American grapes. So vast quantities of North American grapevine roots were imported into Europe, and the local vines were grafted onto these resistant roots. The grapes from the grafted local vines were thought to have virtually the same flavour as before, and to be unaffected by growing on top of an American vine root. Even so, the Burgundy vineyards wanted to protect their reputation, and banned any North American varieties until 1887.

However, the writing was on the wall for absinthe. Thanks to absinthism becoming a major and increasing social problem, absinthe was banned in Switzerland in 1908. In the USA, it was regarded with such horror that it was banned in 1912 — two years before heroin and cocaine were banned. And it was even banned in its natural home of France in 1915.

At the time, absinthism was blamed on a specific chemical called thujone. This thujone was found in the wormwood herb used to make absinthe.

But now, in the 21st century, absinthe is legally available in most of the Western world, provided that the thujone level in the bottle is less than 35 ppm (parts per million).

Thujone — Part 1

So, can thujone cause fits? Yep, it is true that thujone in concentrated amounts can cause convulsions, as well as other medical problems.

In one case, a 31-year-old man bought some little bottles of 'essential oil of wormwood' via the internet. The supplier sold it as an aromatherapy oil — something to be smelled, *not* drunk. But the buyer drank a 10 ml bottle of the oil. Shortly afterwards, his father found him having convulsions, and he became disoriented, lethargic, belligerent, agitated and incoherent. The concentrated wormwood oil had also begun to destroy his muscles — the breakdown products of which had entered his bloodstream and clogged up his kidneys, causing temporary kidney failure. He also had congestive heart failure. Thanks to rapid medical treatment, he recovered and was discharged from hospital after nine days.

One of the toxins in wormwood oil has been identified as alpha-thujone. Normally the human brain runs in a delicate balance, poised between too much and too little activity. Natural chemicals present in the human brain regulate it by slowing it down and

Wormwood and Thujone

The name 'wormwood' comes from the belief that this plant would fight worms living in your gut. Way back in the first century BC, Pliny the Elder wrote in his *Historia Naturalis* that wormwood had this action. Even way back then, he noted that the use of wormwood as a medicine was an ancient practice.

Wormwood is also mentioned in the *Book of Revelations* 8: 10–11: 'A great star from heaven, burning as if it were a lamp, and it fell upon the third part of the rivers, and upon the foundations of waters; and the name of the star is called Wormwood: and the third part of the waters became wormwood; and many men died of the waters, because they were made bitter.'

Wormwood is first mentioned in the Ebers Papyrus, dating back to between 3550 and 1550 BC. It is also mentioned in three of Shakespeare's plays.

The active ingredient in wormwood is a chemical called thujone ($C_{10}H_{16}O$). It is found, in varying levels, in most species of *Artemisia*, a genus of the daisy family. Thujone is also found in other plants such as tansy, sage and white cedar.

However, the main sources of this chemical are regular wormwood (*Artemisia absinthium*) and Roman wormwood (*Artemisia pontica*). The plant is a herb with a perennial root system, with firm, leafy branched stems that reach to a height of 0.6–1 m. Wormwood has tiny globular yellow–green flowers and silver–grey leaves. Oil of wormwood (containing thujone) is extracted from all parts of the plant.

speeding it up. One of the 'slow down' chemicals is GABA (gamma-aminobutyric acid). Alpha-thujone blocks the natural inhibitory action of GABA, leaving the nerves able to fire off too easily.

Therefore, the ingestion of too much wormwood oil will definitely cause convulsions.

Thujone — Part 2

So, did thujone cause absinthism?

Almost certainly not, according to Dr Dirk W. Lachenmeier from the Chemical and Veterinary Medicine Investigation Laboratory in Karlsruhe in Germany.

First, some varieties of wormwood (e.g. those from the Spanish Pyrenees) that are used to make absinthe have zero levels of thujone.

Second, the levels of thujone found in the tested bottles of absinthe were much too low to cause absinthism. Dr Lachenmeier tested 13 bottles of pre-ban absinthe and found their average level of thujone to be 25 ppm, with the highest only 48 ppm. To get the absinthism effect from the thujone, you would have to drink so many litres of absinthe that its alcohol content would kill you first.

Furthermore, we still have some of the recipes that were used to make absinthe in the old days. Typically, low amounts of dried

Essential Oil

If you go to a weekend market and follow your nose, you may end up at a stall selling a variety of essential oils.

These oils are originally stored as microdroplets in the glands of plants. They diffuse through the walls of the glands to spread over the surface of the plant and evaporate, filling the surrounding air with a perfume.

In most cases, we do not know the function of these essential oils in the plants.

But we use them as deodorisers, for adding flavour and, in some cases, as pharmaceuticals.

wormwood were added, which would give the low levels of thujone measured by Dr Lachenmeier.

No, *alcohol* caused absinthism — in other words, absinthism was plain old alcoholic poisoning. While whisky and other spirits rate at 40–50% alcohol by volume, absinthe was typically 70%, and has been measured at 90% alcohol. The alcohol level needs to be so high to ensure that the essential oils are dissolved. This keeps the liquid clear, not murky. When ice-cold water (part of the ritual) is added to the absinthe, some of the oils come out of the solution and make the drink cloudy. This milky opalescence is given the exotic-sounding name of *louche*.

The demon alcohol by itself can account for all the symptoms of absinthism. In his article 'Thujone — cause of absinthism?', Dr Lachenmeier wrote: 'Thujone plays none, or only a secondary role, in the clinical picture of absinthism.' And, of course, some of the adulterants of the day — e.g. copper salts and antimony trichloride, which were used to enhance absinthe's colour, clarity and flavour — were themselves poisonous.

In the early 20th century, absinthe also became a scapegoat. It was often blamed for deaths caused by 'embarrassing' conditions — such as sexually transmitted infections like syphilis — to protect the good name of the family of the deceased.

So perhaps the worm has turned to wipe the slate clean on wormwood — and to dispel the cloudy reputation of absinthe as well.

Aphrodisiac

Among its many fabled qualities, absinthe was also claimed to be an aphrodisiac. This encouraged the late 19th century English poet Ernest Dowson to write: 'I understand that absinthe makes the tart grow fonder.'

References

'About Absinthe', *The New York Times*, 30 July 1882.

Arnold, Wilfred Niels, 'Absinthe', *Scientific American*, June 1989, pp 86–91.

Hesser, Amanda, 'A modern absinthe experiment', *The New York Times*, 31 May 2000.

Hutton, Ian, 'Myth, reality and absinthe', *Current Drug Discovery*, September 2002, pp 62–64.

Lachenmeier, Dirk W., et al., 'Thujone — Cause of absinthism?', *Forensic Science International*, 2006, Vol 158, pp 1–8.

Loubère, Leo A., *The Red and the White: A History of Wine in France and Italy in the Nineteenth Century*, Albany: State University of New York Press, 1978, pp 154–167.

Padosch, Stephan A., et al., 'Absinthism: A fictitious 19th century syndrome with present impact', *Substance Abuse Treatment, Prevention, and Policy*, 10 May 2006, pp 1–14.

Richardson, Dr, 'Absinthe', *The New York Times*, 3 August 1879.

'The charms of absinthe: The allurements it holds out to its victims, and the sting that comes afterwards, confessions of a Frenchman who succumbed to it', *The New York Times*, 19 October 1884.

Wesibord, Steve D., et al., 'Poison on line — acute renal failure caused by oil of wormwood, purchased through the internet', *The New England Journal of Medicine*, 18 September 1997, pp 825–827.

Wu, C., 'Toxin in absinthe makes neurons run wild', *Science News*, 1 April 2000, Vol 157, No 14, p 214.

Bromide and Libido

Back in my high school days, I was in the School Cadets. Every now and then we would go to a real Army Base for Advanced Training. It was there that we heard from the regular Army soldiers that 'someone' put bromide in the soldiers' food to keep their sexual libido way down. Indeed, in his book *Sex and the British*, the author Paul Ferris refers to the use of bromide to reduce the sexual libido of soldiers.

However, as is so often the case with commonly repeated rumours, it's not true.

Lack of Libido

The myth that new recruits are so virile that they need to be tamed and contained by drugs is a backhanded compliment to the soldiers.

This fable of drugging soldiers into docility is well known to various military recruits around the world. In Poland it's the soldiers' coffee that has supposedly been treated, while in France the story is that soldiers are given adulterated wine. South African recruits reputedly have a mysterious substance called 'blue-stone' added to their food to keep them calm, while German recruits are allegedly kept in line with a double dose — the addition of iodine to their coffee as well as soda to their meat.

tAKING thE BANG
Out OF thE 'cANNon'

It has been long thought that 'someone' put bromide in Army food
so as to keep the soldiers' sexual libido way down –
effectively taking the 'bang' out of their 'cannon'.

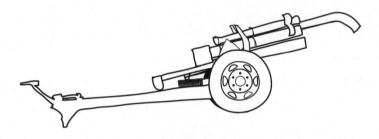

An illustrative interpretation of a soldier's 'limp cannon'

BROMINE

Bromine itself is one of the 92 or so elements – it belongs to the
halogen family of five elements. These halogens also include fluorine,
chlorine, iodine and the rapidly decaying radioactive element called astatine.

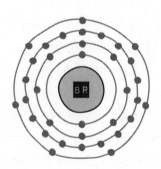

And in many English-speaking countries, if the anti-libido additive is not bromide, it's saltpetre (potassium nitrate).

Bromine — Part 1

Bromine is one of the 92 or so elements. It belongs to the halogen family of five elements, which also includes fluorine, chlorine, iodine and the rapidly decaying radioactive element called astatine.

The word 'halogen' comes from the Greek root *hal*, meaning 'salt', and *gen*, meaning 'to produce', because they all produce sodium salts which are very similar. The best known sodium salt is sodium chloride — common table salt.

There is a difference between 'bromine' and 'bromide'. 'Bromine' is the pure naked element. A 'bromide' is the compound you get when you combine the element bromine with another element, or a group of elements. (In a similar way, 'chlorine' is an element, while 'sodium chloride' is the compound produced when sodium and chlorine have been combined.)

In general, halogens are very reactive, and tend to form strong acids such as HCl (hydrochloric acid) and HF (hydrofluoric acid). Hydrofluoric acid is so reactive that it will react with microscopic quantities of water in glass and actually eat the glass. For this reason, it has to be stored in special water-free glass, or containers lined with beeswax or Teflon™, or containers made of metals that immediately form a layer of inert fluoride (such as copper or steel).

Bromine is, apart from mercury, the only element that is a liquid at room temperature. It is a deep red, fuming liquid with a reddish-brown, acrid poisonous gas. As a liquid it is toxic and causes flesh burns. Some bromine compounds can cause damage to the ozone layer, and are therefore being phased out of production.

Bromine — Part 2

Bromine was discovered independently by two chemists.

In 1825, the chemist Carl Jacob Löwig separated bromine from a natural spring in his home town of Bad Kreuznach in Germany. In 1826, the French chemist Antoine-Jérôme Balard isolated bromine from the residues left in sea salt, after sea water had been evaporated. Bromine occurs at a low level in sea water, approximately 0.06–0.07 g per litre. (In the Dead Sea, the concentration is over 100 times greater — about 5 g per litre.)

Balard published his results first, and so got all the credit. The French Academy of Sciences gave this element the name 'bromine' from the Greek word *bromos*, meaning 'bad or pungent odour' or 'stench of goats'.

Current world production of bromine is about 550,000 tonnes each year. Between 1928 and 1975, most bromine was used to make ethylene dibromide, which was added to the leaded petrols of the day to remove lead deposits from the inside of engine cylinders. Today, ethylene dibromide is used as a pesticide.

Bromine is also used in fire retardants and to make various dyes, while silver bromide is used to make photographic film (the stuff they used before digital cameras). Bromine was used in the printing industry, and so the word 'bromide' can also mean 'a reproduction or piece of typesetting on bromide paper'. And tiny amounts of potassium bromate improve the baking characteristics of wheat flour.

Bromine — The Sedative

The bromides of lithium, sodium, potassium, calcium, strontium and ammonium have also long been used in medicine because of their sedative effect. This could perhaps be the origin of the bromide myth. In the 19th century, these salts of bromine were used as sedatives to treat everything from mild difficulty in falling asleep to full-blown epilepsy. The dose was somewhere between 0.3 and 2 g, and given several times a day, to 'reduce the excitability of the brain'. Indeed, another meaning for the word 'bromide' is 'a trite or unoriginal idea or remark, typically intended to soothe or placate', in other words, bromides create the illusion of wellbeing.

In fact, in the 19th century, children of the upper classes were surreptitiously fed salts of bromine to sedate them, calming down the natural vigour and exuberance of youth. It was delivered to them via their own personal salt shaker at the table, which was supposedly there as a mark of the children's importance and status within the family — but was really there to keep them quiet, and in their place. This made it surprisingly easy to have 'good' children who complied (while lying around doped to the eyeballs) with the old adage: 'Children should be seen, but not heard.'

So, if salts of bromine (the bromides) do have any effect in reducing libido, it's mainly as a minor side effect of their prime use as a sedative. In other words, after taking bromide, you would have a very sleepy person on your hands, not a fully alert person with a mysteriously absent libido.

If there is a lack of libido in military recruits, it is more easily explained by their extreme exhaustion, anxiety, change of lifestyle and close contact with many other similarly exhausted colleagues.

Spike Milligan, who served with the British Army in World War II, had his own take on the effects of bromide. In his book *Rommel? Gunner Who?*, Spike wrote: 'I don't think that bromide had any lasting effect, the only way to stop a British soldier feeling randy is to load bromide into a 300 lb shell and fire it at him from the waist down.'

Born to the Purple Reign

The phrase 'born to the purple' today means somebody born into a wealthy, powerful and noble family. But 2,500 years ago, it specifically referred to especially powerful members of the Imperial Family. In the 4th century BC, the Greek historian Theopompus of Chios wrote that 'purple for dyes fetched its own weight in silver at Colophon . . . in Asia Minor'.

This purple story relies on our New Best Friend, bromine.

Back then, purple dye was incredibly rare. At the time, there was only one source, the predatory sea snail gastropod *Murex brandaris*. If you poke or disturb this 60–90 mm long gastropod, it will squirt a yellow mucous secretion from its hypobranchial gland. This secretion can be processed to yield the purple dye, which was called 'Tyrian Purple' because the snails were first harvested around the sea port Tyre, in what is now southern Lebanon. The dye could also be extracted by crushing the snail's shell; however, you could do this only once. By annoying the snail you could get the dye as often as you liked. It took about 12,000 snails to produce 1.4 g of Tyrian Purple – which was only enough to dye the trim of a cloak.

The Phoenicians were the first to extract this dye. The production and use of this Tyrian Purple was very tightly controlled by the elite. It was also called 'Imperial Dye' or 'Imperial Purple', because its use was restricted to the nobility. The Greeks and the Romans prized the dye, partly because it did not fade. In his *Natural History*, Pliny the Elder wrote: '. . . the Tyrian hue . . . is considered of the best quality when it has exactly the colour of clotted blood, and is of a blackish hue to the sight, but of a shining appearance when held up to the light; hence it is that we find Homer speaking of "purple blood".'

In the 1700s and 1800s, various related sea snail species that produced a similar purple dye were discovered (in the eastern Pacific and the western Atlantic oceans).

The chemical name of this dye is 6,6'-dibromoindigo – and as you can tell from the 'bromo' in the name, it contains bromine. The chemical formula was discovered only as recently as 1909, by the chemist Paul Friedlander.

Flat Tyre

From 2,000 to 4,000 years ago, the Phoenicians used Tyre as a port. The city originally had two parts – one on an island about 800 m off the coast and another on the mainland.

Tyre and its inhabitants suffered mightily at the hands of Alexander the Great.

He laid siege to it for seven months, and finally took it in 332 AD. He completely wiped out the mainland city, then used the rubble to construct an enormous land bridge – approximately 180–270 m wide and 800 m long – from the shore to the city on the island. He then executed 10,000 citizens and sold another 30,000 into slavery.

The land bridge still stands today.

References

Encyclopaedia Britannica, 2008 Ultimate Reference Suite — 'Murex', 'Tyre', 'Theopompus of Chios' and 'Heracles'.

Mikkelson, Barbara, 'The saltpeter principle', Urban Legends References Pages, 13 August 2001; http://www.snopes.com/military/saltpeter.asp.

'Raising an army', *New Scientist*, 27 April 2002, p 73.

'Raising an army', *New Scientist*, 29 June 2002, p 65.

Sports Drinks

(Electrolyte up my Life)

In general, exercise is a good thing. When you exercise vigorously, you usually get hot and sweaty, lose some body water and perhaps become a little dehydrated. So what is the best way to replenish this lost fluid? This is where it gets tricky.

Some people think that they should guzzle down plain water to rehydrate.

However, other people believe the exact opposite to be true. They believe that plain water is dangerous because it can flush essential electrolytes from their bodies and upset their metabolic balance. This is why they choose a sports drink to rehydrate.

Yet another group believe that it is impossible to drink too much.

However, none of these beliefs is entirely true.

Dehydration Can Kill

Yes, dehydration can kill you — indeed, each year nearly two million children under the age of five die from dehydration brought on by infectious diarrhoea. In severe cases, water alone cannot rehydrate you — you need water with the right amounts and types of sugars and salts added.

This knowledge is not new. The great Indian physician and surgeon, Sushruta — a truly wise person — was aware of this 2,500 years ago. He was skilled in nose and eye surgery and was the first person known to operate on bladder stones. He knew of heart pain (angina), seemed to understand the concept of blood flow in arteries and veins, and accurately described the illnesses leprosy, diabetes and hypertension.

He also recommended that infectious diarrhoea be treated by drinking not plain water, but rather a mixture of rice water, carrot soup and coconut juice. He was right. Plain water was not the best fluid for treating infectious diarrhoea, such as that caused by cholera.

In fact, it was the modern treatment for cholera, based on Sushruta's traditional ideas, that led to the first generation of sports drinks.

Cholera Today?

Amazingly, the disease cholera still exists today.

According to the World Health Organization in 2002, about '88% of diarrhoeal diseases in the world are attributal to unsafe water, sanitation, and hygiene'.

In July 1994, thanks to yet another war, over half a million Hutu refugees were interned in a camp in Zaire in Africa. Over 12,000 died from cholera. The death rate of those infected with cholera was about 50%, 'as a result of inadequate supplies of water, sugar and salts'.

There was an outbreak of cholera in Zimbabwe in late 2008. By April 2009, about 100,000 people had been infected, and about 4,000 had died.

Cholera — Natural History

Cholera is the illness caused by the bacterium *Vibrio cholerae*. It is usually spread by drinking water contaminated with this

it's enough to give you the ......

Cholera is the illness caused by the bacterium *Vibrio cholerae*.
It is usually spread by drinking water contaminated with the bacteria.
The infective dose in healthy adults is about 100 million bacteria.
The incubation period is about 1.5 to 5 days.
It kills people by giving them such copious diarrhoea, that they dehydrate.

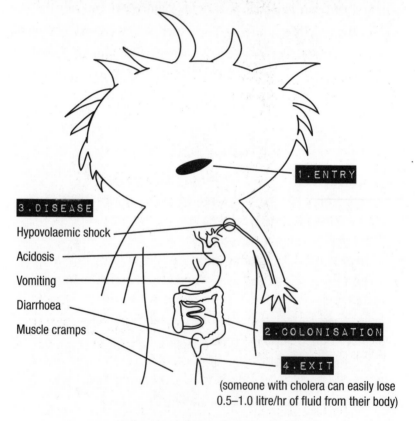

1.ENTRY

3.DISEASE

Hypovolaemic shock

Acidosis

Vomiting

Diarrhoea

Muscle cramps

2.COLONISATION

4.EXIT

(someone with cholera can easily lose
0.5–1.0 litre/hr of fluid from their body)

The modern treatment for cholera
led to the first generation of sports drinks.

bacterium. The infective dose in healthy adults is about 100 million bacteria, with an incubation period of about 1.5 to 5 days. It kills people by giving them such copious diarrhoea that they become severely dehydrated.

The bacterium makes a toxin (Cholera Toxin) that poisons the cells lining the gut. (By the way, to medical people, the gut is the hollow 10 m long tube that begins at the mouth and finishes at the anus.) These cells then exude — into the hollow pipe of the gut — huge quantities of a liquid rich in sodium, potassium and

ChOLerA toXIn

(a simplified view)

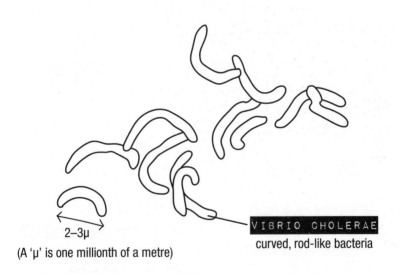

2–3μ

(A 'μ' is one millionth of a metre)

VIBRIO CHOLERAE
curved, rod-like bacteria

The bacterium makes a toxin (Cholera Toxin) that poisons
the cells lining the gut. These cells then exude
(into the hollow pipe of the gut) huge quantities
of a liquid rich in sodium, potassium and bicarbonate.
The amount of liquid secreted is too much for the
lower gut to re-absorb. The victim dehydrates rapidly
thanks to their producing vast quantities
of the so-called 'rice water stools'.

bicarbonate. The amount of liquid secreted is too much for the lower gut to re-absorb. The victim dehydrates rapidly thanks to their producing vast quantities of the infamous, so-called 'rice water stools'. Someone with cholera can easily lose 0.5–1 litre/hr of fluid from their body.

Cell Membranes

The amount of water that crosses the cell membranes in the human body is simply astonishing.

Water molecules jump into the Red Blood Cells (RBCs) and then out again, and then in again, and so on. They do this very frequently. In fact, in just one second, a volume of water equal to about 100 times the volume of the RBC passes in and out of the RBC membrane. Obviously, these are mostly the same water molecules jumping in and out, over and over again. Assuming that you have about 2 litres of RBCs, this means that a total of about 17 million litres of water go in and out of your RBCs each day – that's 17,000 tonnes of water!

This 17,000 tonnes of water is just for the 2 kg of RBCs. The tonnage of water must be correspondingly higher for the remaining kilograms of your body.

With such a huge flow, you need only a slight interference with the flow in one direction to rapidly over-hydrate or dehydrate you.

As a personal example, I knew one woman who suffered from pre-eclampsia (nothing to do with diarrhoea, but lots to do with keeping too much water in the tissues). The 'cure' for pre-eclampsia is immediate delivery of the baby. After delivering her lovely baby (in a bit of a hurry), she then urinated away 10 litres of water that same day, and another 10 litres over the next two days.

Incredibly, in some cases, the patient can actually die of dehydration *before* they have their first episode of diarrhoea — this is called Cholera Sicca. In these victims, the poisoned cells that line the gut dump litres of fluid into the hollow pipe that is the gut. This fluid cannot be re-absorbed into the bloodstream. In Cholera Sicca, this happens so quickly that the victims do not have time for a bowel motion. In fact, they die before they even go to the toilet. When a cholera pandemic hit Paris in 1831, it killed so many people so quickly that François Magendie, the French physiologist, wrote that it was 'a disease that begins where other diseases end, with death'.

Typically, the death rate for cholera is about 50% if untreated, and 1% if treated. In India alone, between 1816 and 1917, nearly 30 million human beings died from cholera. Most deaths from cholera occur on the first day of infection.

The disease will resolve itself in a few days, when healthy gut cells replace the poisoned ones. However, in the 50% of cases of untreated cholera that lead to death, the victim dies from dehydration before the poisoned cells can be replaced.

Cholera — Treatment

You would think that the treatment for massive diarrhoea from cholera would be easy — simply replace the water at one end as fast as it is being lost from the other end. But it doesn't work like that. The problem is that the water you drink does not get absorbed by the gut.

Giving water to cholera victims only increases the loss of water as rice water stools. The 'replacement' water does not leave the gut to enter the bloodstream, it just passes through until it leaves the 'other end'. And, all the time, the victim is losing water and electrolytes that desperately need to be replaced.

Gut Absorption

Human beings are approximately 45-75% water. One of the body's major 'water pumping stations' is the small intestine.

Surprisingly, the small intestine is not short. It makes up about 70% of the gut. It is called 'small' because it is narrow, with an internal diameter of about 2.5–3.0 cm. It has a massive surface, thanks to all the folds on its inner surface – 250 square metres, instead of just 0.5 square metres if it were a smooth tube.

The small intestine begins at the end of the stomach and finishes before the large intestine. (The word 'stomach' does not mean 'all that stuff between the bottom of the ribs and the top of the legs'. Instead, I use the word 'stomach' in its anatomical sense, as the organ between the oesophagus and the small intestine.)

It absorbs water and nutrients through the cells that line it, sending them to the bloodstream.

However, under certain circumstances, the small intestine can stop absorbing.

Each day, you take in about 1.5 litres of fluid. Your gut secretes a further 7 litres or more, giving a total of 8–9 litres per day.

Your small intestine normally absorbs about 7 litres each day, leaving 1.5 litres to enter the colon. But, if required, your small intestine can absorb about 20 litres or more each day (as well as lots of nutrients). And your large intestine can absorb even more water (but virtually no nutrients). Overall, absorption is greater, leading to relatively dry faeces.

However, in diarrhoea, the normal balance is upset, with a combination of increased secretion from the gut wall and/or reduced absorption from the gut wall.

> Either way, diarrhoea is defined by the World Health Organization as 'passage of loose or watery stools at least three times in a 24-hour period'. But their definition also emphasises the importance of change in stool consistency.

The first scientific approach to the problem of cholera deaths occurred in 1831. At the age of just 22, Dr William Brooke O'Shaughnessy, an Irish doctor, scientist and inventor, read out to the Westminster Medical Society the results of his analysis of the blood of cholera victims in India. He discussed how dehydrated the 'thick, cold, black blood of cholera' was, and said that this might be reversed by injecting suitable fluids directly into the veins. He published his observations in *The Lancet* in December that year. (Dr O'Shaughnessy also introduced medical uses of marijuana to Western medicine and received a knighthood for his later work on electric telegraph systems.) In June 1832, Dr Thomas Latta, following on from Dr O'Shaughnessy's work, published in *The Lancet* a recounting of the first successful use of intravenous (IV) rehydration to treat the diarrhoea of cholera.

The principle was simple: a needle was inserted into a patient's vein, and large quantities of sterile water gradually dripped into the vein. But still, it did not always work. Why? Because in many cases the treatment was not aggressive enough — too little fluid was entering the patients' veins. In addition, the fluids themselves were often unsterile, chemically impure and not formulated to the same 'saltiness' as blood.

But even if the IV fluids were sterile and pure, and given in large enough quantities, they were still very expensive. So even today, IV treatments are not really suitable for the mass treatment of cholera diarrhoea.

Cholera Resistance

Surprisingly, a person can be somewhat resistant to cholera. There are at least two factors – blood type and the inherited disease cystic fibrosis.

We do not fully understand why, but there appears to be a spectrum of resistance to cholera based on blood type – AB being most resistant, followed by Type A, then Type B, with Type O the most susceptible.

We partially understand the link to cystic fibrosis. In cholera, the bacterium *Vibrio cholerae* makes proteins that interfere with the movement of chloride and sodium ions, so that a huge surplus of these ions remain in the gut. These ions have an osmotic action, and drag water from the bloodstream into the gut. From there, the easy way out is down to the anus and so the rice water stools gush forth.

In the disease cystic fibrosis, there is a defect in the transport of ions across cell membranes. This defect lessens the harmful effect of the cholera bacterium.

Oral Rehydration Therapy — Theory

If only there were a way to 'trick' the cholera-infected gut into absorbing water.

It turned out that there was — and it depended on a scientific discovery.

Only as recently as the 1950s did Western physiologists realise that there are two quite separate mechanisms for absorbing water from the gut into the bloodstream — a Passive Mechanism as well as an Active Mechanism.

In the Passive Mechanism, the water simply diffuses down a concentration gradient — or a 'gravity gradient' if you want to be

How Much Sugar?

To allow the Active Mechanism to carry water across the gut wall into the bloodstream, the level of glucose in the water needs to be around 3%. The Active Mechanism will not work any faster at higher concentrations.

But some of the so-called sports drinks have glucose levels as high as 9%. This is to provide fuel for muscle and brain (typically 30–80 g/hr). But a level this high can actually lead to a loss of electrolytes and slow the absorption of water.

It can also possibly increase the risk of tooth erosion. Increased tooth erosion occurs when you drink small quantities frequently. The sugars remain in the mouth for a while, becoming a food supply for bacteria. The mouth needs time to restore its balance after each drink. If you have one small drink, and then another small drink, the mouth does not get a chance to restore itself. Unfortunately, this is how sports drinks are commonly drunk. So athletes are often advised to squirt the drinks towards the back of the throat, rinsing with water afterwards, both during and after their exercise sessions, in order to take good care of their teeth.

The Position Paper of the American College of Sports Medicine recommends that sports drinks have 4–8% sugars, with 6–7% being optimal.

This provides the best compromise between intestinal absorption and fuel supply, i.e. between fluid and fuel.

technical — in the same way that a ball rolls down a hill. This Passive Mechanism doesn't work in cholera victims, because the cells lining their small intestine are poisoned.

The Active Mechanism can shift 10 to 100 times more water than the passive one. It needs both glucose and sodium to work, and uses these chemicals to drag water out of the gut into your body. (It can work with fructose instead of glucose, but it will just run more slowly.)

ORT — Practical Theory

By the 1960s, this knowledge led to the first modern use of Oral Rehydration Therapy (ORT). ORT is just a fancy name for carefully measured salts and sugars dissolved in germ-free water. In the early 1960s, Dr Robert A. Phillips used ORT to treat patients with cholera. But this did not attract the attention it deserved in medical circles.

One of the first major (and widely recognised) uses of ORT happened as a result of the Indo–Pakistan War in 1971. Wars always affect civilians, and nine million refugees had poured into India from Pakistan. One refugee camp alone held one-third of a million refugees. Overcrowding led to poor hygiene and, ultimately, cholera. Intravenous (IV) therapy for the cholera worked, but was so expensive that only very few patients could be treated using this method. In the refugee camps where IV therapy was being used, the death rate for cholera victims was still 25%. It was so high because most of the patients who needed IV therapy actually did not get it, simply because the medical staff had run out of costly IV sets and the costly sterile fluids.

Something had to be done. Dr Dilip Mahalanabis knew that Dr Phillips had previously used ORT successfully. He and other doctors took over the Johns Hopkins Medical Library in Calcutta (now Kolkata), set up assembly lines to weigh out the ingredients in the correct proportions, poured them into plastic bags, and sealed them with a hot iron. They then used non-medical volunteers (the friends and relatives of the patients) to add the salts to clean water and administer the salty liquid orally to the patients.

ORT Solution

There are several variants of Oral Rehydration Therapy (ORT) solution. A typical commercial 1 litre preparation would contain:

- 2.6 g of sodium choloride (NaCl, to replace lost sodium)
- 2.9 g of trisodium citrate dihydrate ($Na_3C_6H_5O_7.2H_2O$, to correct the acidosis that comes with diarrhoea, and to help the absorption of sodium)
- 1.5 g of potassium chloride (KCl, to replace lost potassium)
- 13.5 g of anhydrous glucose ($C_6H_{12}O_6$, to help the water cross from the gut into the bloodstream).

If a commercial solution or an ORT sachet is not available, you can get by with adding to 1 litre of water:

- 8 level teaspoons of common sugar
- 1 level teaspoon of table salt.

You can also add half a cup of orange juice or mashed banana for its potassium content.

Sports drinks are not a substitute for ORT for clinically dehydrated people — although they would be better than plain water.

First, they contain too much sugar. Their higher sugar level (around 6%) is fine for refuelling, but it also slightly delays transfer of water from the gut into the bloodstream. (The so-called energy drinks can carry more than 8% sugars, which can delay gastric emptying.) Second, they have too few electrolytes. If their electrolyte level were high enough to act as an ORT drink, they would taste too salty.

ORT — Practice

When ORT was used, the death rate in cholera victims dropped from 25% to 3%. This occurred because the treatment worked in most cases, and it was cheap enough to treat most of the patients.

In 1978, *The Lancet* wrote that ORT is 'potentially the most important medical discovery of the 20th century'.

Worldwide, the average child under the age of five has 2.2 episodes of diarrhoea each year. In 1980, the number of children under the age of five dying each year from diarrhoea was 4.6 million. By 2000, the widespread use of ORT had reduced this to 1.8 million per year. Today, approximately 500 million ORT sachets are made each year — one for every 13 people on the planet.

In the field (away from a hospital), a sachet of various carbohydrates and salts — and sometimes proteins — is added to 200 ml of clean drinking water and simply drunk by the sick person. Oral Rehydration Therapy can be used to treat previously fatal dehydration — and is a far cheaper, and more easily deliverable, treatment than intravenous fluids.

ORT does not reduce the diarrhoea. The diarrhoea continues as before, or even at a greater rate, because the patient is not getting dehydrated — and still has water in the body that can generate rice water stools.

But at least the patient does not die from dehydration.

Childhood Killers

What are the major causes, worldwide, of death in childhood?

In one survey of health professionals, 40% named the major childhood killers as AIDS, tuberculosis and malaria.

However, in reality, the three major killers of children are pneumonia, diarrhoea and malaria.

Birth of Sports Drinks

The medical research into ORT led to the development of the now popular 'sports drinks'. One of the very first commercially available sports drinks was Gatorade. It was, like ORT, a combination of carbohydrates (sucrose, glucose and fructose) and electrolytes (sodium and potassium), with added lemon or lime (to improve the flavour).

However, the composition was different from ORT. It had a higher carbohydrate content (because it was designed to refuel both muscle and brain as well as enhance intestinal fluid absorption). And it had a lower sodium concentration (to make it more palatable).

It was formulated in 1965 by Dr R. Cade at the University of Florida, to support the Florida Gators Football Team, who, at that time, were on a losing streak. American Football games last for hours, and in the hot and humid climate the players sweated massively and suffered from mild dehydration. The energising and rehydrating effects of the sugars and salts in the Gatorade did help the Florida Gators in the crucial second half of their games. In 1967, for the first time, the Gators won the coveted Orange Bowl.

The Kansas City Chiefs, from Missouri, also had problems with their players flagging in the second half. They too tried Gatorade, which was credited with helping them achieve impressive victories.

Use of Sports Drinks

Some 40 years later, sports drinks are big business. In fact, Gatorade has — after a few legal battles — earned over $80 million for the University of Florida.

By the way, in the bottled drink trade, the sugars and salts are known as 'pixie dust' or 'fairy dust'.

Sports scientists all agree that a little pixie dust does help water absorption. It also helps to maintain your 'Thirst Drive'. The salts make you feel thirsty, and/or the flavouring makes it more delicious — either way, you drink more.

They also agree that highly trained athletes who sweat a lot each day, thanks to several hours of hard exercise in a hot environment, need sugars to provide fuel for the muscles and brain, and electrolytes and water to replace the losses from heavy sweating. Indeed, many athletes struggle to consume sufficient carbohydrates to meet their daily needs. These athletes would include marathon runners, large football players and tennis players who train for long hours.

But do the rest of us need sports drinks?

To answer that question, you need to realise that the goal of drinking during exercise is to replace the water lost from sweating (and other water losses, such as from urination).

Sweat 101

When you don't exercise, your kidneys manufacture urine at 20–1,000 ml/hr. But during exercise, the kidneys decrease their rate of manufacture of urine.

How much you sweat is very variable. It depends on environmental conditions — wind and sun exposure, temperature, humidity, sky and ground radiation, etc. It also depends on local conditions — your metabolic rate, your metabolic efficiency (how much work you produce for a given effort), your body weight, your clothing, how hard you work, your history of heat acclimatisation, etc.

Sweating is the major pathway for removing heat during vigorous exercise in warm to hot weather. (Actually, it's the evaporation that removes the heat, but you have to sweat a liquid onto your skin before you can evaporate it away.) People working hard can generate 1,000 watts. If their metabolic efficiency is 20%, then they have to get rid of 800 watts continuously, which requires the generation of about 1.2 litres of sweat.

Sweat contains both water and salts. The salts include 5 milliequivalents per litre (mEq/litre) of potassium (range 3–15), 1 mEq/litre of calcium (range 0.3–2), 0.8 mEq/litre of magnesium (range 0.2–1.5) and 30 mEq/litre of chloride (range 5–60).

The effect of sweating is to remove water from the body, i.e. to reduce your Total Body Water (TBW). Your TBW ranges between 45% and 75% of Total Body Mass, the average being 60%. Your TBW is generally regulated to within +/− 0.2–0.5% of Total Body Mass. However, during the post-ovulation phase of the menstrual cycle, women can increase their Total Body Mass by up to 2 kg (due to increased water retention).

But with exercise in hot conditions, a sudden drop of 2% in TBW degrades aerobic and mental performance to an easily detectable level. This 2% drop is a strong warning signal that the athlete is entering a potentially dangerous zone.

Warning – Numbers Ahead!

800 watts = 0.8 kW = 0.8 kJ/sec = 48 kJ/min = 11.46 kcal/min.

Assume that this heat energy is dissipated by evaporating sweat (which is close to 100% water).

The Latent Heat of Evaporation of water = 2.43 kJ/g = 0.58 kcal/g.

So a sweating person who generates 800 watts of waste heat needs to evaporate about 20 g of water/sweat each minute. This works out to about 1,200 g/hr, or 1.2 litres per hour.

Sports and Stress

The effect that different sports have upon the body ranges from relatively non-stressful (such as lawn bowls or billiards) to very stressful (such as marathon running).

How stressful? Consider a person with a fever so excessively high that it is almost lethal. Their metabolism can increase by 100% above normal. But medium-distance runners can increase their metabolism by 2,000% above normal — and survive. Some sports, if continued for too long, can be lethal if they interfere too much with your electrolyte levels, or cause hyperthermia (extremely high body temperature).

What You Need

You need sugar if you burn lots of energy and electrolytes if you have lost some via sweating. This is because sweat removes mainly sodium from your body.

Depending on the sport, there are four possibilities with regard to sugar and electrolytes. You will need (1) sugar and electrolytes; or (2) just sugars; or (3) just electrolytes; or (4) neither sugar nor electrolytes.

In the first situation, a person needing both sugar and electrolytes might be a marathon runner, who will burn energy *and* sweat a lot. Marathon runners, American Football players and male competition tennis players can sweat fluids at over 2 litres/hr.

In the second situation, a person needing mainly extra sugar might play a so-called intermittent sport in cold weather. They stop and start a lot, and so burn up energy, but might not sweat a lot. Depending on the position played, this could be someone in amateur soccer or tennis. Mind you, 'serious' amateurs could push themselves hard and sweat a lot, and so be shifted up to the first category of needing both sugar and electrolytes.

A person in the third category — who would need only electrolytes (and water, of course) — might be an athlete sweating in a sauna, in order to keep their weight down to a class limit. This can be dangerous if the person takes the dehydration too far — and is not recommended.

People who go for a 10 minute jog around the park every morning fall into the fourth category. They would not really need any extra sugar or electrolytes, just H_2O. On the other hand, they might enjoy the taste of the sports drink (even though it's more expensive than petrol, volume for volume).

Advantages of Sports Drinks

Sports physiologists agree that some athletes in prolonged exhaustive sports definitely need a combination of sugars and salts. Sports drinks also help athletes engaged in moderate to intense activity of an hour or more. Athletes also hydrate better with a sports drink — they tend to consume more, and the water is better absorbed. And if the athlete is low on energy before the start of the event, the carbohydrates in the sports drink can help maintain the glucose levels in the blood better. And, surprisingly, just having the taste of sugars in the mouth can make athletes perform better.

Test cricketers can get dehydrated after a hot day of intermittent activity, mostly spent standing on the cricket field. Surprisingly, there have been cases where the cricketers did not rehydrate overnight, and so began the next day on the cricket field already slightly dehydrated. Sports drinks could help here.

Sports physiologists also agree that drinking pure water does not flush away electrolytes, and that most people who exercise for less than an hour do *not* need sports drinks.

Rinse Mouth to Perform Better!

It seems perfectly reasonable that you can improve your sports performance by consuming some fuel (e.g. sugars). But, strangely, it also seems that you get the same effect from simply rinsing it around your mouth, and then spitting it out!

The study was carried out by Dr E.S. Chambers and colleagues from the School of Exercise and Sports Science at the University of Birmingham in the UK. They worked with eight trained cyclists, who had fasted for six hours. The cyclists had to perform at 75% of their maximum workload for about one hour. They swished their mouths with a liquid eight times during that hour and, on each occasion, spat it all out into a bowl after ten seconds. The liquid either contained sugars or, if it had no sugar, it tasted sweet thanks to the addition of saccharin and aspartame (artificial non-calorie sweeteners).

The results were amazing. When the exercising cyclists swished their mouths with saccharin/aspartame water, they performed at a certain level. But when they swished 6.4% carbohydrate (sugar) solution in their mouths, their performance improved by an astonishing 2–3%.

Why? We don't really know. We do know that individual muscle fibres will fatigue after lots of work. And we also know that there is some poorly understood central brain control of 'fatigue'. Another part of this study looked at brain activity. It found that a part of the brain involved in 'reward' became active when the mouth experienced a swish with the sugar solution.

Drink Too Much ...

Sports physiologists also agree that it is possible to drink too much.

A tragic example of this occurred in the 2002 Boston Marathon. (Coincidentally, sports scientists wrote a paper in *The New England Journal of Medicine* on that very marathon.)

A few months before the marathon, newspaper advertisements for a major sports drink encouraged marathon runners who might enter to drink at least 1,200 ml/hr, or else '... your performance could suffer ...'. A marathon is the classic case where a sports drink can help. Two-thirds of the 766 runners provided a blood sample at the end of the marathon. Of those, about 13% had drunk so much liquid — more than they had lost in sweating, breathing, etc — that they had actually gained weight and had diluted their blood sodium to somewhat worryingly low levels. Low sodium levels cause symptoms that include: 'headache, vomiting, swollen hands and feet, restlessness, undue fatigue, confusion and disorientation (due to progressive encephalopathy), and wheezy breathing (due to pulmonary oedema). When plasma sodium falls ... (further) ... the chances increase for severe cerebral oedema with seizure, coma, brainstem herniation, respiratory arrest, and death.' One competitor, 28-year-old Dr Cynthia Lucero, actually died because her sodium levels were too low, from drinking too much. The autopsy report stated that her death was due to 'ingesting too much Gatorade'.

Mind you, death can also happen by drinking too much fluid of any type, and in situations unrelated to sport. Fatalities have occurred in workplace drug testing (where people have tried to 'flush' drug residues out of their bodies to avoid detection in their urine samples) or drinking contests (such as a radio station-sponsored competition in which the last person 'standing' before having to urinate wins a prize). And it's always more of a risk with those who have a smaller body mass (e.g. women).

Indeed, some people wrongly think that it is impossible to drink too much, and that drinking too much cannot harm you.

It is important to understand your body, and how it behaves in any sport you do, and to drink the correct amount (not too much, not too little). You can use your change in body weight as a guide, and assume that a loss of 1 kg means that you have lost 1 litre of sweat. It's a rough approximation, but it's close enough.

You Might Need It …

Yes, sports drinks have their advantages — especially if you work out for an hour or more. And, of course, they can help if you sweat profusely.

One study looked at voluntary drinking in boys who were exercising hard for a few hours in the heat. If the water had some added flavouring, it tasted nicer so they drank more of it and did not get so dehydrated. And water with added carbohydrates and salt prevented the dehydration altogether.

However, you don't have to sweat huge amounts to benefit from a sports drink. There is mounting evidence that taking carbohydrates immediately before and during high-intensity events lasting an hour or more can enhance performance. If you are a swimmer training for two hours at a time in temperate water, you may not sweat a lot, but the extra fuel is helpful. The swimmer could, of course, eat a meal, but it's quicker and easier to drink rather than eat when you are training hard. The sports drink also has the benefit of being optimised for quick emptying from the stomach.

Besides helping those engaged in one-hour sports with low to moderate sweat losses, sports drinks can also help those in long events in cooler weather (e.g. cross-country ski events).

You Might Not Need It ...

Water drinks (with additives) are *hot*.

There are dozens of different brands in petrol stations, gyms, supermarkets and health food shops all waiting for you to buy them. But the majority are not proper sports drinks, with the appropriate amounts of sugars and salts. They are merely flavoured water with added caffeine or just plain flavoured water — all promoted with lots of advertising.

Good sports drinks that are well formulated (e.g. Gatorade and Powerade) do help athletes who regularly exercise for an hour or more. They can be very useful. But they do not do a lot for the person who goes for an occasional short jog. The discriminator for the beneficial use of sports drinks is your physiological need. For example, if you exercise at a moderate to high intensity for an hour or more, you need to consider whether you need to replace brain and muscle fuel, or fluids, or both.

So yes, rehydrate with sports drinks when you exercise for an hour or more in warm conditions, but not too little or too much, or else you will risk watering down all your hard work. And if you exercise only occasionally, and just for a short time, leave the pixie dust to the fairies ...

Dehydrated = Mad

Our family has spent a lot of time in the Outback. We have, over the years, crossed 15 of the 17 deserts in Australia.

Way back in 1993, we were at the Three Ways Roadhouse near the Gulf of Carpentaria having a feed. I ran into a bloke called David, who had ridden in on a battered motorbike. We got talking and, after a bit, he told me how he and his mate Ken had ridden their bikes along the full length of the Canning Stock Route a few years earlier.

I was pretty surprised, because this stock route is hard going. It runs some 2,000 km between the top right-hand corner of Western Australia, and the lower left-hand corner, in a mainly north–south direction.

The reason they survived was because they had a rule that they wouldn't go to sleep until they had a wee.

David (on a 600cc XT Yamaha Ténéré) and Ken (on a Honda XR 500) started at Halls Creek and headed south along the Canning Stock Route to Meekatharra. It took them two weeks.

They were well prepared. They timed it so that their trip centred around the full moon in October 1987. This was so that if things got bad, they could ride out at night to either the east or the west, to the nearest town. They rode in two shifts – from 3 am to 11 am, and from 4 pm to 6 pm. In the middle of the day, they rested.

Each bike had 25 litres of petrol in the tank, and carried two 20-litre jerry cans as well. They used 60 of their precious 65 litres getting to Well 35. (There are 51 wells, from Well 1 at the southern end to Well 51 at the northern end.) They had arranged for a 200-litre fuel drop at Well 35, and took on 120 litres, but had to leave 80 litres behind.

They didn't carry an emergency radio – there's not a lot of room on a motorbike.

They each carried a total of 20 litres of water, in various containers. It wasn't a lot of water, but they filled up at the three or so wells that they passed each day. They were drinking 25 litres each per day. Riding a motorbike in sand is like jogging, because you're standing up all the time, so you work hard and get thirsty.

They ate army rations (one Day Pack each day, $25 each) because they were nutritionally well balanced, and because the rations were not dehydrated. If they ran low on water, they didn't want to have to use it to rehydrate food.

They wore compasses on their arms, and mounted strip maps of the stock route on their handlebars. And their lives were saved because of the rule that they had made on a previous occasion while riding across the Simpson Desert.

They'd noticed that even though sometimes they were actually quite thirsty, they didn't drink enough water. And so they made up a rule that they simply would not go to sleep unless they had urinated. You see, in most cases your body will let you urinate *only* if you are well hydrated (body fluid balance is actually a very complicated field of study, but this short sentence is a mostly correct summary).

It turned out to be a pretty rough trip. It was 43ºC at Alice Springs, and it had to be hotter than that along the route. It was so hot that the valves in the engine stuck.

Early on, around the third and fourth days, they each got injured. Ken hit a termite mound with his right foot. (When a four-wheel drive vehicle travels the Canning Stock Route, it follows the wheel tracks, and only a few centimetres or so of mudguard actually projects outside the wheels. But on a motorbike, a lot of the motorbike and your feet project out on either side of the wheels.) Ken took his shoe off that night. His foot swelled up overnight, and he could hardly get his shoe back on the next morning. So he left his right shoe on for the rest of the trip. The next day, David broke three toes on his right foot, and he left his right shoe on for the next week.

A few days later, at the 11 am stop, they arrived at an empty well. They had each drunk 15 litres of water, and had only 5 litres each left. They didn't stop, and pushed on to the next well which was quite close, only about 20 km away.

They soon began to experience heat exhaustion. David described it as the feeling you get when you drink five nips of rum really quickly. He was breathing very fast, felt dizzy, and was so uncoordinated that he kept falling over. But because they were so irrational from the dehydration caused by the heat exhaustion, they just kept on riding and falling over, and riding and falling over, sustaining more injuries with each fall, and laughing uproariously at the fun of it all. They arrived at the next well (which luckily had water) around midday.

'We decided we deserved a rest after that, so we didn't do the evening run.' They lay down and rested, and drank. 'When you're buggered, you don't feel like drinking, but you know you have to,' David said. So they stuck to their rule and kept on drinking water. Gradually their heads became clearer, and they realised what terrible shape they were in, and how close they had been to death. But they still hadn't urinated so they kept on drinking. And finally after sundown, around 8 pm, eight hours after they had started resting and drinking, they finally urinated and went to sleep.

When they woke up the next morning, they realised how dehydrated and delirious they had been. If they hadn't drunk water until they had urinated, they could have easily died. They might have woken up the next morning still delirious and dehydrated (and not known it). They could easily have ridden and fallen and laughed until they died. Or they might have become even more dehydrated during the hot night, and not have woken up in the morning.

When I was talking to David up at the Three Ways Roadhouse, at first I couldn't understand his rule of not going to bed until he urinated. But when I thought about it, I realised that it probably saved his life. David still rides motorbikes. But Ken sold his motorbike after their trip, and took up rowing instead.

References

Almond, Christopher S.D., et al., 'Hyponatremia among runners in the Boston Marathon', *New England Journal of Medicine*, 14 April 2005, pp 1550–1556.

Chambers, E.S., et al., 'Carbohydrate sensing in the human mouth: effects on exercise performance and brain activity', *Journal of Physiology*, 15 April 2009, pp 1779–1794.

Chatterjee, Asok, et al., 'Evaluation of a sucrose/electrolyte solution for oral rehydration in acute infantile diarrhoea', *The Lancet*, 25 June 1977, pp 1333–1335.

Gerlin, Andrea, 'A simple solution', *Time*, 8 October 2006, pp 40–46.

Guerrant, Richard L., et al., 'Cholera, diarrhea, and oral rehydration therapy: triumph and indictment', *Clinical Infectious Diseases*, 1 August 2003, Vol 37, No 3, pp 398–405.

Guyton, Arthur C. and Hall, John E., *A Textbook of Human Physiology*, 9th edition, Pennsylvania: W.B. Saunders Company, 1996, pp 43–55, 183–187, 297–313, 833–844, 1059–1070.

Harris, Jason B., et al., 'Blood group, immunity, and risk of infection with *Vibrio cholerae* in an area of endemicity', *Infection and Immunity*, November 2005, Vol 73, No 11, pp 7422–7427.

Noakes, Timothy David and Speedy, Dale B., 'Lobbyists for the sports drink industry: an example of the rise of "contrarianism" in modern scientific debate', *British Journal of Sports Medicine*, February 2007, Vol 41, Issue 2, pp 107–109.

Place, Nicolas, 'Go rinse your mouth: a novel way to improve endurance performance?', *Journal of Physiology*, 1 June 2009, pp 2425–2426.

Sack, David A., et al., 'Cholera', *The Lancet*, 17 January 2004, pp 223–233.

Sawka, Michael M., et al., 'Exercise and fluid replacement', *Medicine & Science in Sports & Exercise*, February 2007, Vol 39, Issue 2, pp 377–390.

Thapar, Nikhil, et al., 'Diarrhoea in children: an interface between developing and developed countries', *The Lancet*, 21 February 2004, pp 641–653.

Wilk, Boguslaw, et al., 'Effect of drink flavor and NaCl on voluntary drinking and hydration in boys exercising in the heat', *Journal of Applied Physiology*, April 1996, Vol 80, Issue 4, pp 1112–1117.

TANGLed HAIr

(A Knotty ProBLem)

Considering that we humans are basically hairless apes with a big brain, we spend a lot of time worrying about the small amount of hair sitting on the top of our heads. The money spent on hair products is huge. As a result, hair product companies have — from what I have seen in their TV ads — the best laboratories with the most beautiful and/or manly scientists that money can buy.

So, how did these huge hair product companies not notice that you get more tangles in straight hair than in curly hair? Or if they did, why didn't they tell us?

Hair 101

The hair on our scalp insulates us long-limbed mammals against heat loss, and protects us from the Sun.

Each individual hair can support an 80 g weight. So if you could weave all of your 100,000–150,000 scalp hairs into a single rope, it could hold up an 8–12 tonne truck.

Each individual hair is a long, thin fibre made of keratin. Keratin is the tough and insoluble protein found in hair, wool, fur, skin, silk, horns, fingernails, porcupine quills, and hoofs — and even some hair shampoos. There are different types of keratin — some hard, some soft.

First, a bunch of smaller amino acids (mostly glycine and alanine) join together to make each individual keratin protein. The shape of the keratin protein is like a helix, or spiral staircase. Four of these helices twist around each other to make a protofibril. In turn, eleven protofibrils are bundled together to make a microfibril, which in turn are bundled together to make a macrofibril, which in turn are bundled together to make a hair shaft.

Each individual hair shaft is made by a single hair follicle. You have about 100,000–150,000 hair follicles on your scalp when you are born — and that's all you will ever have. Thanks to the nerves that surround each of these follicles, you know when your hair brushes against something.

The hair follicle is special — it's one of the very few organs in an adult that regenerates in a cyclical fashion.

Colour of Hair

The colour of hair usually comes from a pigment called melanin. (Once again, as is always the case with the human body, everything is more complicated than first thought. There are actually different types of melanin: eumelanin is the most common and gives the shades from brown to black, and pheomelanin gives the yellow-blond and red colours.)

Black hair contains lots of melanin, while light brown and blond hair contains less. And the hair of people with albinism contains no melanin at all.

But red hair is special. Not only does it contain melanin, it also contains some iron. So 'rusty' is actually a scientifically correct nickname for someone with red hair.

ShAFt's the nAMe

Cutaway of the microscopic structure of a
human hair shaft.

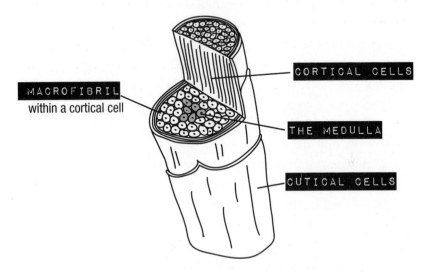

CORTICAL CELLS

MACROFIBRIL
within a cortical cell

THE MEDULLA

CUTICAL CELLS

And, a diagram of a hair follicle.

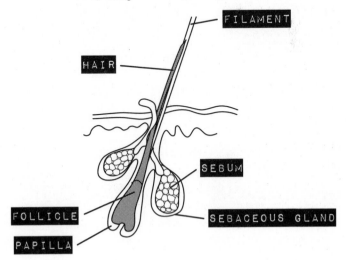

FILAMENT

HAIR

SEBUM

FOLLICLE

SEBACEOUS GLAND

PAPILLA

Baldness

About 40% of men go bald.

In males, baldness is programmed by the male sex hormone, testosterone. The testosterone gets converted into dihydrotestosterone (DHT). In youth, DHT puts hair on males. But in later years (and we don't know why), DHT has the completely opposite effect. It seems to shut down the follicles that have lots of DHT receptors. In fact, some men with very high levels of testosterone go bald at an early age. (Surprisingly, not only do some follicles have the receptors for DHT, they carry the enzyme that converts testosterone to DHT. This makes them 'Suicide Follicles', carrying the means of their own loss of function.)

A hair follicle has only a limited number of cycles of growth and rest before it stops working – probably around 25 or so. (Once again, we don't know why.) The hair product company L'Oréal studied ten men over a 14-year period in the 1980s and 1990s. They shaved off the 200–300 hairs in just one single square centimetre on each man's head, and counted how many of the hairs grew back, and how quickly they did so. They found that men who tended to go bald early had hair follicles with very short cycles of growth and rest. It seems to be a case of Live Fast and Die Young for some cases of baldness.

Getting back to testosterone, if a male is castrated at a very early age (i.e. before puberty), he never makes any large amounts of testosterone. So the castrated male, a eunuch, will never go bald.

Hair 102

Each hair follicle manufactures its hair shaft from the base (unlike plants, which do most of their growing at the tip). Hair follicles have a long growing period, followed by a short resting period.

The follicle grows hair for up to five years in women, but only three years in men. In that time, a single hair can grow 75 cm in a woman, but only 45 cm in a man (roughly 10–15 mm per month). This is why women can grow their hair longer than men can.

After the growing period comes to an end, the follicle takes a rest for about three months and shrivels up. The root of the hair is now very shallow, only about half a millimetre below the surface. At that stage, the hair shaft can be easily pulled out by a comb, or a strong wind, or by rubbing against something. At any given time, about 10% of the hair follicles are resting.

The hair follicle then wakes up and starts growing a new hair. This new hair pushes out any old hair still stuck in the follicle.

We still don't know the working of the mechanism that stops these cycles from being synchronised in the hair follicles. But it's good that they are not synchronised. If they were, all of our hair would fall out at the same time, instead of at the steady rate of 50–100 hairs each day.

Hair Tangles — A Knotty Problem

It was a French physicist who first took this new look at hair.

He needed a problem for his students. In fact, this preliminary study of his was originally aimed at high school students, to get them interested in science. This is why it's more a preliminary study, rather than a fully developed work.

He started thinking about scalp hair, which is a collection of about 100,000 individual shafts. He thought that perhaps it might be possible to model this complex system of 100,000 separate units in a simple way.

Even today, there is still no single widely accepted model that predicts how hair will behave. And there is so much that we still do not know about 'tangles' — e.g. how they form, how they resolve, why they form here rather than there, and why there are sometimes so few or so many.

Hair Tangles — Theory

He developed a theory of geometric modelling of hair, setting up a simple model based on the science of polymer dynamics.

He made a few assumptions. First, he modelled straight hair (or a bunch of straight hairs) as a rigid segment with a known length. Curly hair was modelled as having a straight section and a wavy section. Second, he assumed that these hair strands are fixed into the scalp at one end but point in all possible directions at the other end. A hair can also change from pointing in one direction to pointing in any other direction. And, third, he assumed that any two hairs, or any two groups of hairs, can cross each other, and they can do so at a variety of angles.

There were other assumptions as well. The hairs are also subject to random turbulence. They can move independently of each other. But occasionally they can also move in a coordinated motion — as in the ads on TV, when the female model's metre-long hair falls like a slow-motion wave.

The hair product industry has its special language to describe hair — but so does science. 'Oily' made the physicist think of 'cluster formation and binding energy', while 'straight and curly' started him ruminating on 'general geometry and spatial

BAd HAIr DAy

STYLISH OR
BAD HAIR

BIG BRAIN
SHOULD BE
LOCATED HERE

Human beings are basically hairless apes
with big brains.

organisation'. 'Thin and thick' was more than just a description
of diameter — to a physicist, it was 'the influence of elementary
characteristic properties on general behaviour'.

His theory predicted that straight hair should have more tangles
than curly hair. This is the opposite of what you would expect.

Hair Tangles — Experiment

Theory is one thing, but experiment is another.

His experiment involved two hairdressers checking for tangles
in the hair of their clients, for three weeks. They checked 212
people (123 with straight hair, and 89 with curly hair) in the late
afternoon between 4 and 7 pm. This time was specifically chosen
to allow the maximum time and opportunity for the hair to tangle
after a hard day of waving about in the breeze and rubbing against
the trees.

In science, you need definitions. Therefore, a 'tangle' was defined as a 'cluster or grouping of hairs that resist combing'. This excluded natural clusters of hair, such as a curl or a ringlet. To find any tangles, the hairdressers used a comb with a 3 mm separation of the teeth.

The experimental results were astonishing — on average, 5.3 tangles were found in each head of straight hair, but only 2.9 for curly hair.

At this stage, we still don't fully understand what is going on.

Why More Tangles with Straight Hair?

The initial theory implies that the shafts of straight hair cross each other less often than do the shafts of curly hair. Now this is reasonable, because you would think that the straight hairs would tend to stay parallel to each other, and not cross each other.

But the physicist's theory also told him that when the straight shafts do cross, they do so at a greater angle than for curly hair. Perhaps this is the clue — the critical factor. Human hair does not have a perfectly smooth surface. A microscope shows that the surface is coated with fish-like overlapping 'scales' with shallow notches.

Perhaps these scales 'lock' into each other only when the hair shafts cross each other at a large angle?

Perhaps the individual strands in curly hair tend to move as a single unit, while the strands in straight hair tend to move individually?

The 'worst' hair for tangling is dry, fine, chemically treated hair. With this type of hair, perhaps the scales stick to each other very easily? Unfortunately, this early model does not yet account for this fine detail.

Why is Pubic Hair Curly?

This question came up on the Triple J Science Talkback show. I was perfectly honest, and said that I did not know, but that I would go looking for an answer.

I came up with a whole bunch of potential reasons. Obviously, not all of them would carry the same weight, and some of them could even be wrong. But, for better or for worse, here are some of them:

1   Maybe because pubic hair is located in a warmish moist environment, and is scrunched up all the time.

2   Maybe it's caused by the sulphur in the proteins that make up the keratin in hair. Pubic hair possibly has more sulphur, and this sulphur can carry a charge, which can give the proteins in hair a 'twist'. Perhaps this 'twist' gets carried up from the micro scale to the macro scale.

3   Maybe it's caused by the shape of the hair shaft. Apparently, in cross section, the shape of scalp hair is a circle – so it will resist a bending force equally well in all directions. And again, apparently, the cross-sectional shape of pubic hair is like an oval. In the longer direction, this cross section is very strong and quite resistant to bending, but in the shorter direction it is quite weak and susceptible to bending. Anyhow, for what it's worth, this is another possible (but not necessarily true) reason.

4   The sex hormones act on the hair follicles in the genitals to make them generate curly hair – perhaps via oval exit holes for the hair.

5   Perhaps curly hairs trap pheromones (hormones that leave the body to travel to another body).

6   Perhaps pubic hair is curly to stop it poking you in the eye ...

7   ... and other silly reasons.

Anyhow, the next week I came back on air and ran through these ideas hoping that the truth was somewhere in there ...

But then a sex worker from Kings Cross phoned in to Triple J and said that she had noticed (in her line of work) that Asians tended to have straight pubic hair. And the next phone call was from a sports coach who was shepherding a group of Japanese sportsmen around Australia. He had noticed in the showers that they had straight pubic hair. And he said that his female counterpart had noticed the same phenomenon in the Japanese sportswomen travelling with them.

So my line of thought was limited by my Western point of view. But, seeing as how pubic hair is becoming a thing of the past with all the Brazilian waxes going on down there – as opposed to out there – this research may never get the public attention it deserves.

We still don't know where this research will take us. But perhaps it will lead to better Velcro-type materials, because Velcro involves hairy fibres crossing each other and hopefully getting entangled. Or perhaps the large hair product companies will swing the resources of their massive laboratories to finally solving the vexing problem of tangling hair. After all, the problem of tangled hair is a curly one ... Or perhaps they aren't too fussed about splitting hairs!

References

Kunzig, Robert, 'The biology of ... hair: zeroing in on the molecular switches that regulate hair growth', *Discover*, February 2002.

Masson, Jean-Baptiste, 'Why does curly hair get less tangled than straight hair', *American Journal of Physics*, August 2007, Volume 75, Issue 8, pp 701–706.

Nicholson, Christie, 'Straight hair is knottier than curly hair', *Scientific American*, 13 March 2008.

FLAt EArth

(ThE Truth Is On thE hOrIzOn)

There are many false perceptions about what happened in bygone eras. One of the most common ones is that before Columbus, everybody believed that the world was flat. This is not so! The inhabitants of Medieval Europe (back in the 15th century) did not believe that the Earth was flat and that Columbus would simply sail off its edge.

In fact, people have known the Earth to be a ball (or a sphere) for a long time.

The biographer Samuel Eliot Morison wrote in his Pulitzer Prize-winning biography of Christopher Columbus: '... for of all the vulgar errors associated with Columbus, the most persistent and the most absurd is that he had to convince people "the world was round". Every educated man in his day believed the world to be a sphere, every European university so taught geography, and seamen ... knew perfectly well that the surface of the globe was curved.'

History of Round Earth

About 2,500 years ago, Pythagoras (c. 582–c. 507 BC) postulated that the Earth was spherical, not just a flat circular disc. He did this for aesthetic reasons, because a sphere was supposedly perfect.

'The Last Iconoclast Dies'

This was the headline in *The Fortean Times* when Charles Kenneth Johnson, President of the International Flat Earth Society, died in Lancaster, California, on 19 March 2001.

Samuel Shenton and his wife, Lillian, from Dover in the UK, had founded the International Flat Earth Society in 1956. Charles Johnson became the leader of the society when Shenton died in 1971.

Johnson had embraced the Flat Earth belief when he was just eight years old. 'When I was at school, the first maps I saw were flat. Then Roosevelt flooded all the classrooms with globes. Well, I didn't believe it.'

He maintained that our world was a circle of unknown size, with the North Pole in the middle, the South Pole on the circumference, and the whole thing surrounded by a wall of ice approximately 50 m high (the Antarctic ice). The Moon and the Sun, he claimed, were the same size – about 50 km across – and they circled above the disc of the Earth at a height of about 4,800 km. They didn't touch the sky, which itself was a dome reaching to a height of about 6,400 km. And sunrise and sunset – easy, just optical illusions.

Aristotle (384–322 BC) agreed. But he had some experimental evidence.

First, there are the lunar eclipses, where the shadow of the Earth falls on the Moon. These happen at many different times — when the Moon is close to the horizon, or when it is high in the sky. So, if the Earth were a flat disc, every now and then there would be a lunar eclipse in which the light of the Sun would hit the supposed disc of the Earth at an angle, not square on. This would produce an ellipse on the surface of the Moon. But, instead, every lunar eclipse has the Earth throwing a circular shadow onto the Moon. Aristotle wrote: 'The sphericity of the earth is proved by the evidence of … lunar eclipses. For whereas in the monthly phases of the moon, the segments are of all sorts — straight, gibbous (convex), crescent — in eclipses, the dividing line is always rounded. Consequently, if the eclipse is due to the interposition of the Earth, the rounded lines result from its spherical shape.' The conclusion is obvious — the Earth has to be spherical.

Second, said Aristotle, sailors knew that when seeing a distant ship, they would first glimpse the top of the mast before sighting the rest of the ship. Once again, this shows that the Earth has to be round.

And, third, some southern constellations rise only a little above the horizon in the Northern Hemisphere. But, said Aristotle, when travellers went further south, they saw these constellations rise higher in the sky. This could not happen with a flat Earth — but could with a spherical Earth.

About a century later, Eratosthenes of Cyrene (c. 276–c. 194 BC), the Third Librarian of Alexandria, did some very simple geometry based on the length of shadows. He estimated the circumference of the spherical Earth — and got very close to the correct figure!

And well into the next millennium, around 830 AD, the Muslim astronomer al-Farghani, working with other astronomers of Calif al-Ma'mun, undertook a series of measurements. They measured the Earth's circumference as being 40,253 km — within 0.5% of the current figure of 40,075 km.

Measure Size of Earth with Sticks

Eratosthenes was a Greek who lived in Alexandria in the 3rd century BC. Using just a stick and some maths, he measured the circumference of the Earth.

He had been told by travellers of something wonderful in the Egyptian town of Syene (situated near the giant dam on the Nile, today it is known as Aswan). On just one day of the year, the Summer Solstice, the light of the Sun would reflect off the water in the bottom of a well, for a few moments around midday. That meant that on the Summer Solstice, the Sun was vertically overhead (and that Syene was on the Tropic of Cancer). So on the same day, 21 June, Eratosthenes set up an experiment in his home town of Alexandria. He set up a stick to be perfectly vertical and, around midday, measured the smallest shadow that it threw. The shadow was about 7.2° away from the stick. Now, 7.2° is about one-fiftieth of the 360° that make up a circle.

So that meant that the distance between Syene and Alexandria was one-fiftieth of the circle that makes up the Earth (roughly 800 km).

All Eratosthenes had to do was find the north–south straight line distance between Syene and Alexandria. This came to about 5,000 stadia (one stadia was the length of a foot race in a stadium).

If 5,000 stadia represented one-fiftieth of the circumference of the Earth, then the full circumference was 250,000 stadia.

But a few assumptions were made.

First, Syene was not exactly on the Tropic of Cancer, but slightly north of it. So the Sun was not exactly vertical on the day of the Summer Solstice.

Second, Syene was not exactly south of Alexandria, but a little to the side – so the measured north-south distance between them was a little inaccurate.

Third, the Sun is not a point infinitely far away, so its rays are not exactly parallel. Indeed, over the distance between the Earth and the Moon, they diverge by one-sixth of a degree.

Fourth, it is really difficult to maintain accuracy when you have to pace out a distance of 800 km.

Fifth, how big was a stadia in those days? How many ruined stadiums do you have to average? The Greek historian Herodotus (c. 484 BC–c. 425 BC) reckoned that one stadia was 600 feet. But how big is a foot? Depending on the purpose of the measurement, and which culture measured it, a stadia could range between 157 m and 209 m. So the circumference of the Earth would range from about 40,000 km to about 46,000 km.

Anyhow, depending on the exact measurements used and other factors, Eratosthenes got to within 0.5–17% of the true value – which is pretty good using just a stick as the measure!

Eratosthenes – Always Second Best

Eratosthenes spread himself over many fields. Besides being an astronomer, a geographer and a mathematician, he was also a poet and an athlete. He worked out the circumference of the Earth, and the tilt of its spin axis. He also devised a system of latitude and longitude, and a calendar that included leap years.

His colleagues called him 'beta' (the second letter of the Greek alphabet), because they reckoned he was the second best in almost any field.

Myth of Flat Earth

So, for the past 2,500 years, in Europe and in the Middle East, the Flat Earthers were in a very small minority.

At least, this is what the historian Jeffrey Burton Russell, of the University of California at Santa Barbara, believes. His book *Inventing the Flat Earth: Columbus and Modern Historians* claims that since the 3rd century BC, practically all educated people in the Western world believed in a spherical Earth.

Looking into the historical record as an historian, he found tens of thousands of Christian theologians, poets, artists and scientists who believed that the Earth was a sphere. On the other hand, he could find only five Christian authorities who believed in a Flat Earth. Dr Russell wrote: 'In the first fifteen centuries of the Christian era, five writers seem to have denied the globe, and a few others were ambiguous or uninterested in the question. But nearly unanimous scholarly opinion pronounced the Earth spherical, and by the Fifteenth Century all doubt had disappeared.'

In fact, Dr Russell found that the myth was started in the 1830s by a Frenchman and an American, acting independently. One was anti-Church, the other anti-British.

The Frenchman was Antoine-Jean Letronne (1787–1848), an antireligious academic of great renown. He wrote *On the Cosmographical Ideas of the Church Fathers* in 1834, in which he deliberately misrepresented medieval Christians as being scientifically ignorant. His supposed proof for this claim was that they believed in a Flat Earth. But this was untrue — they did not believe in a Flat Earth. (Mind you, in Galileo's time, the Church persecuted him for advancing a model of the Universe without the Earth at its centre.)

The American whom Dr Russell refers to started his myth-making six years earlier than Antoine-Jean Letronne. He was

Washington Irving (1783–1859), who wrote his history of Christopher Columbus in 1828.

Microsoft and Flat Earth

According to the online BBC News Magazine, Microsoft used the Flat Earth metaphor in an advertisement in mid-2008.

'Depicting an olden-days ship sailing on rough seas, presumably heading towards the "edge of the world", the advert is part of a $300m campaign aimed at rescuing the reputation of Windows Vista by comparing its critics to flat-earthers.'

Why Rewrite History?

The year 1828 was a good time for Americans to revisit their European history — and rewrite or, at the very least, change its emphasis.

Around this time, the British were quite adamant that it was a Brit, Sebastian Cabot (c. 1476–c. 1557), who first made landfall in North America.

This could almost be correct, if you ignore the Scandinavians, who got there a few centuries before Cabot. You also have to ignore the fact that Cabot claimed (depending on whom he was speaking to) that he was born in England, or in Venice — so he may not have been British at all. In 1497, Sebastian may (or may not) have travelled with his father, John Cabot, on the ship *Matthew*, under the patronage of the English King Henry VII, to North America. The ship made landfall on 24 June, somewhere around southern Labrador, or Newfoundland, or Cape Breton Island. They believed that they had landed in China.

This British claim rankled with the Americans, who were not especially friendly with the British at that time. (There was that little matter of the War of 1812 between the USA and Great Britain, which lasted from 1812 to 1815.) So it made sense to shift the emphasis to Columbus 'discovering' North America.

This was the beginning of the reinvention of Columbus as the Mighty Discoverer of America. In truth, Columbus, in all of his four voyages, had never set foot on the North American continent. The closest he had come to the mainland was some small islands in the (West) Indies, well off the coast.

But Who's the Man to Do It?

This was very good timing for the American author Washington Irving. He was probably the first American author to earn his living entirely from writing and one of the first who was confident enough to place the locations of his stories in the USA, rather than Europe. He wrote for the person in the street, rather than for the academic. His stories, written in the vernacular, were intended to entertain, rather than to enlighten. For this reason, his stories 'The Legend of Sleepy Hollow' and 'Rip van Winkle' were wildly successful with the general public.

In 1826, while he was in Paris, he received a letter from Alexander Everett, the US Minister to Spain, inviting him to Madrid. A huge archive of documents relating to Columbus had been painstakingly assembled over a period of more than 35 years, and they were about to be published — in Spanish. Everett suggested that Irving translate these into English, for American readers.

Irving agreed, initially seeing this task as a speedy translation job. But once he began to read the archives, he changed his focus to writing the first major biography of Columbus for the American public.

However, his aim was always to entertain, not educate. He didn't read all of the archives, nor did he read the documents carefully. He saw his task as writing a 'romantic history' rather than an accurate one. And, indeed, such a work would attract more readers than a serious academic work.

His multi-volume work, *A History of the Life and Voyages of Christopher Columbus*, was published in 1828. It was translated into eight languages, and went through 90 printings and editions in Irving's lifetime alone. It was enormously popular.

Batman

If you read your comics, and go to the movies, you will have heard of Batman. Batman hangs out in Gotham City, keeping it safe for its citizens. Most people know that Gotham City is just another name for New York City.

Washington Irving (of Christopher Columbus fame) was the person who gave us the name of 'Gotham'. He first used this name in the 17th issue of the literary magazine *Samagundi* on 11 November 1807. 'Gotham' is an Anglo-Saxon word meaning 'Goat's Town'.

He also gave us the phrase the 'almighty dollar'.

A Few Problems

However, Irving's history of Columbus had serious flaws regarding its accuracy.

As one modern historian put it, Irving 'turned the story of Columbus into a work of art'. To make it more interesting, he 'created conversations and monologues; he manipulated chronologies for dramatic effect; he staged scenes of dubious validity'. Through Irving's dramatic narrative, numerous Columbian myths — for example, Queen Isabella's offer of her jewels to fund the first voyage, a near-fatal shipwreck off Lisbon … — reached a widening audience as Irving's work grew in popularity.' Columbus had now become 'a modern rationalist whose 1492 voyage disproves the alleged medieval belief that the world was flat'.

And, of course, these myths were spread by other writers, who did not check the original sources.

Columbus — Westward Ho!

Columbus wanted to sail west to China, Japan and India.

But he made two major mathematical errors — he calculated the world as too small, and Asia as too wide.

His first error was that he used a value for the circumference of the world that was about 75% of the real value. He assumed that Arabic miles measured the same distance as Roman miles. But they were 75% the length — making the Mysterious East 25% closer.

His second error was that he used the wrong coordinates for Asia. As a result, Asia appeared to extend much much further to the East. So if he were to sail to the west on a planet that was spherical, according to his calculations he would run into the Mysterious East after sailing only 5,000 km.

These errors worked together to make it just barely possible to get to the Mysterious East (if it were located where Columbus claimed). You see, his three ships were quite small (between 20.5 and 23.5 m in length), and could not carry supplies for a very long voyage. But if he ran into a landmass before he ran out of supplies, he and his crew would survive. If Columbus was correct with his calculations, it was possible for him to reach Cathay in his tiny ships before running out of food and water.

So Beginnith the Myth

Washington Irving painted a colourful and dramatic word picture of Columbus trying to convince a board of Flat-Earth Inquisitors (the University Council of Salamanca) that the Earth was round, so that he could get funding.

The eminent biographer Samuel Eliot Morison wrote: 'Washington Irving, sensing his opportunity for a moving and picturesque scene, took a fictitious account of this nonexistent university council ... elaborated it, and let his imagination go completely.'

Irving wrote that Columbus had to deal with 'an imposing array of professors, friars and dignitaries ... [who] came prepossessed against him, as men in place and dignity are apt to be against poor applicants'. This Council supposedly argued, by quoting scripture, that the Earth had to be flat. Suddenly (according to Irving), Columbus was in really big trouble. Even though Columbus was deeply religious, he was now in danger of heresy — which could mean being burned alive at the stake.

The Facts

Like all good myths, there is an element of truth here.

Columbus did indeed meet with learned men. But they were not inquisitors and hooded theologians, they were scientists. Furthermore, there was no University Council of Salamanca — just the scientists at the Royal Court of Queen Isabella and King Ferdinand in Salamanca.

The scientists did not argue with him about whether the Earth was round. Nope, all educated people (especially sailors who had to know some astronomy to navigate) knew that the Earth was a ball.

However, the scientists did point out that Columbus's distances for getting to the East by sailing west were wildly inaccurate — the distance was closer to 20,000 km, rather than the 5,000 km claimed by Columbus. The scientists were correct, and Columbus would have perished.

But, luckily, he happened across some islands off the American coast that he called the Indies, believing that he had sailed to India. Dr Russell writes: 'If God or good luck had not put America — the West Indies — in the way to catch him, Columbus and his crews might indeed have perished, not from falling off the Earth but from starvation and thirst.'

The Myth Spreads

Various educational authorities of the day put the Irving version of the Council of Salamanca confrontation in their school textbooks. By the 1860s the myth spread throughout the USA, Europe and elsewhere.

It received an enormous boost after the publication of Darwin's *Origin of The Species* in 1859. Evolutionists unfairly claimed that Creationists believed in a Flat Earth, as an example of how unscientific they were.

Some even used this Flat Earth myth in 'the war between science and religion'. David Noble wrote in his foreword to Dr Russell's *Inventing the Flat Earth* that, 'It was during the last years of the nineteenth century and the early years of the twentieth century, then, that the voyage of Columbus became such a widespread symbol of the futility of the religious imagination and the liberating power of scientific empiricism.'

How times have changed! At least there's one thing that Evolutionists and Creationists can agree on — the Earth is not flat.

HOw tO mEAsurE thE DIstANcE tO thE mOOn wIth A gOIn (ANd A LunAr EcLIPsE ANd A gLOcK)

Warning, Will Robinson, Warning!
Danger, Will Robinson, Danger!

Please feel free to ignore this section, if you feel like ignoring it. It requires about 10 minutes of hard thinking, and maybe a small coffee or tea – and no interruptions. Get comfortable, and turn off your mobile phone. Switch off the radio, the TV, the music – leave nothing firing but your brain. But it's fine to have another human reading it with you at the same time – you can help each other.

If you skip straight to page 100, you won't lose anything.

But if you are able concentrate for 10 minutes, you will know how to measure the distance to the Moon with a coin.

HErE wE GO...

(Note: Diagrams are not drawn to scale.)

Aristarchus of Samos lived from 310 BC to around 230 BC. He measured the distance to the Moon using a lunar eclipse, a clock and simple geometry.

The Ancient Greeks could see that the Sun and the Moon are almost exactly the same apparent size in the sky. (In reality, the Moon is about 400 times smaller than the Sun, but it's about 400 times closer, so it 'appears' the same size.)

1 The Sun and the Moon appear the same apparent size in the sky.

Get a coin (say, 1 cm in diameter). How far do you have to hold it from your eye to exactly block out the Moon? About 108 cm (but you need an exceptionally long arm). Imagine the shape of a cone between your eye and the Moon – this cone is 1 unit across at the base, and 108 units long.

So if you are standing on the Earth, and you look at the Moon, you are setting up a triangle with the height:base ratio of 108:1.

2 If you hold a 1 cm (in diameter) coin on the end of a stick about 108 cm from your eye, it will exactly block out the Sun, or the Moon.

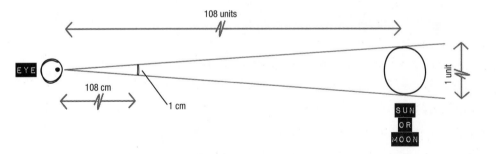

Now the Moon and the Sun look the same size in the sky. So if you look at the Sun, you are again setting up a triangle with the height:base ratio of 108:1.

Just once more – any time you look at the Sun or the Moon, you set up a triangle with a height:base ratio of 108:1.

At this stage, we have to learn a tiny bit about Similar Triangles. In Similar Triangles, corresponding sides are in the same ratio to each other. In the pic below, ABC and EFG are Similar Triangles (because each side in EFG is twice as big as the corresponding side in ABC).

3 Triangles are similar if they have the same 'shape', but not necessarily the same size. You can think of it as 'zooming in' or 'out', making the triangle bigger or smaller, but keeping its basic shape.

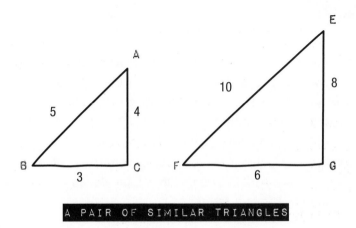

A PAIR OF SIMILAR TRIANGLES

Here's another pair of Similar Triangles – ABC (the big one) and AEF (the little one)

4 ABC and AEF are Similar Triangles.

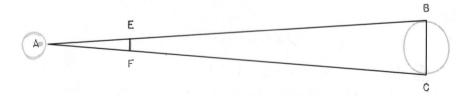

The Sun is a lot bigger than the Earth. So the shadow that the Sun casts behind the Earth has the shape of a cone.

Th₢ sun Is ᴮIGG₢r thAn th₢ ₢Arth

5 The Earth casts a shadow in the shape of a cone.

If you stand at A (which would mean you were mysteriously floating in space), then the Earth (ʙ ᴄ) will exactly block the Sun.

This means (from pic 2) that $\dfrac{AC}{BC} = \dfrac{108}{1}$

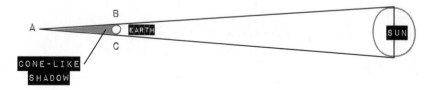

A is the tip of the cone of the shadow of Earth thrown by the Sun. If you stand at A and look at the Earth as it exactly blocks the Sun, the triangle ABC has the height:base ratio of 108:1.

(If you want to be super accurate, the true height of triangle ABC should be measured from the centre of the line, BC. But ABC is a very skinny triangle, so AC is close enough to the true height.)

Eratosthenes measured that the circumference of the Earth is about 40,000 km.

The Ancient Greeks knew that pi, the ratio of the circumference to the diameter, is about 3.14.

So the diameter of the Earth is about 12,700 km.

BACK tO ᴇrAtOsthᴇnᴇs

6 The circumference of Earth = 40,000 km

π = 3.14 = ratio of the diameter to the circumference

Therefore, the diameter of the Earth

$$= \frac{40,000}{3.14} = 12,700 \text{ km}$$

EARTH

We already know that the triangle ABC has a height:base ratio of 108:1.

LᴇNGth OF shAdOw cONᴇ

7 Triangle A B C has a ratio of 108:1 (from pic 5)

Therefore, $\dfrac{A C}{B C} = \dfrac{108}{1}$

But B C = diameter of the Earth = 12,700 km

Therefore A C = 108 x B C
= 108 x 12,700
= 1,372,000 km

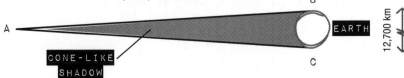

A — B — EARTH — C — CONE-LIKE SHADOW — 12,700 km

So the distance from Earth to the end of the cone of shadow (point A) is about 1,372,000 km.

We now need a person with a clock – a bucket with a small hole in the bottom is good enough, so long as you keep topping up the water to keep it at roughly the same level.

During a lunar eclipse, the Moon moves into, and then out of, the conical shadow of the Earth. It takes about 4 hours (on our modern clocks) for the Moon to cross the shadow. As the Moon cuts into and out of the Earth's shadow, it gets darker and changes colour.

Now count the time between when the Moon first kisses the shadow, and when it is just fully inside – say, 100 drops of water.

Now count the time between when the Moon first kisses the shadow, and when it has just fully left the shadow – say, 250 drops of water.

hOw BiG is thⒺ MOon coMParⒺd to thⒺ width oF ⒺArth's shAdOw?

8

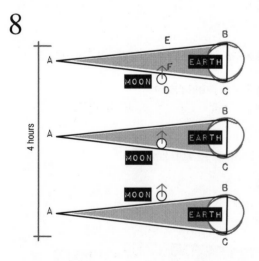

By measuring time with a clock, the Earth's shadow E F is about 2.5 times bigger than the Moon's diameter D F

Therefore, $\dfrac{E F}{D F} = \dfrac{2.5}{1}$

In this instance, the clock is simply water dripping through a hole.

So the width of the Earth's shadow (at EF) is about 2.5 times the diameter of the Moon.

Now it's time to play Similar Triangles.

Triangle ABC is a 108:1 triangle (because you are looking at the Earth exactly blocking out the Sun – from pic 5).

Triangle AEF is a 108:1 triangle (because it is similar to triangle ABC – from pic 4).

Triangle CDF is a 108:1 triangle (because any time you look at the Sun or the Moon, you make a 108:1 triangle – from pic 2).

LuNAr ECLIPsE + sIMILAr trIANGLEs

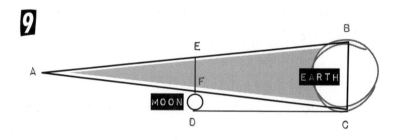

(i)   The Moon travels upward through the cone of shadow on the dark side of the Earth.
(ii) A B C is a 108:1 triangle (from pic 5)
(iii) A E F is a 108:1 triangle (similar to A B C – from pic 4)
(iv) C D F is a 108:1 triangle (from pic 2)
(v)   Therefore A E F and C D F are Similar Triangles

These triangles all have the same height:base ratio – about 108:1. So they are all Similar Triangles.

Now remember that when the Moon crosses the Earth's shadow, the shadow is 2.5 times bigger than the Moon.

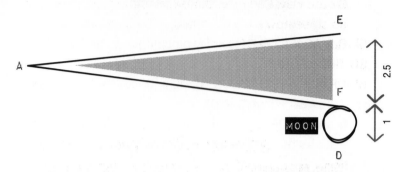

We measured this back in Step 8, using a simple water clock and our eyes.

And now, in six amazing steps, we put it all together to measure the Distance to the Moon.

1) AEF and CDF are Similar Triangles (from pic 9).
2) EF/DF = 2.5/1 (from pic 10).
3) AF/CF = 2.5/1 (Similar Triangles, from pic 9), therefore AF = 2.5 x CF.

An◌ FInALLy, th☰ ◌lstAnc☰ tO th☰ mOOn

11

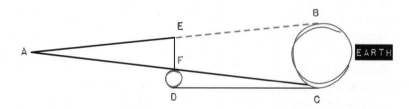

(i) A E F and C D F are Similar Triangles

(ii) $\dfrac{E\,F}{D\,F} = \dfrac{2.5}{1}$ (from pic 10)

(iii) $\dfrac{A\,F}{C\,F} = \dfrac{2.5}{1}$ (because they are Similar Triangles)

(iv) So A C = A F + C F = (2.5 x C F) + C F = 3.5 x C F

(v) But A C = 1,372,000 km (from pic 7)

(vi) Therefore C F the distance to the Moon

$$= \frac{1,372,000}{3.5} = 392,000 \text{ km}$$

4) Now AC = AF + CF. But AF = 2.5 x CF (from Step 3 above), therefore AC = (2.5 x CF) + CF = 3.5 x CF. By the way, CF is the Distance to the Moon. (We are so close now.)
5) But AC = 1,372,000 km (from pic 7).
SO THEREFORE
6) CF = 1,372,000/3.5 = 392,000 km.

CONGRATuLATioNS!
You MeAsureD the distANce to the mooN!

This figure is within a few per cent of the true value! I am so impressed by the wisdom of those Ancient Greeks. Aren't you amazed how 'easy' it was to measure the distance of the Moon! And it took only 10 minutes out of your life (after the Ancient Greeks did all the hard yards).

References

Gingerich, Owen, 'Astronomy in the age of Columbus', *Scientific American*, November 1992, Vol 267, No 5, pp 66–71.

Gingerich, Owen, 'Review of *Inventing the Flat Earth: Columbus and Modern Historians* by Jeffrey Burton Russell', *Speculum*, July 1993, Vol 68, No 3, p 885.

Morison, Samuel Eliot, *Admiral of the Ocean Sea: A Life of Christopher Columbus*, Boston: Little Brown, 1942.

O'Neill, Brendan, 'Do they really think the earth is flat?', BBC News Magazine, 4 August 2008, http://news.bbc.co.uk/2/hi/uk_news/magazine/7540427.stm.

'Passing of an eccentric', *The Skeptic* (Australia), Winter 2001, Vol 21, No 2, p 4.

Russell, Jeffrey Burton, *Inventing the Flat Earth: Columbus and Modern Historians*, New York: Praeger, 1991.

Schlereth, Thomas J., 'Columbia, Columbus, and Columbianism', *The Journal of American History*, December 1992, Vol 79, No 3, pp 937–968.

Lemon Dissolves Fats

In these politically correct times, you have to be careful with your language. For example, it's no longer proper to refer to a popularly believed story as an 'Old Wives' Tale' — instead you have to call it an 'Information Item from a Mature Female Domestic Engineer'.

There is a lot of Useful Knowledge in the general population — there's even a special name for it: 'The Wisdom of the Commons'. But, some of the Information Items that get passed on can sometimes be wrong.

For example, what of the claim that using lemon juice on battered fish is good for you? This claim suggests that the lemon juice destroys or dissolves the fat or oil in which the batter has been fried. This dissolved fat, with all of its kilojoules, is supposed to vanish magically, leaving you with a slim waist.

That's a lot to ask from a lemon.

History of the Lemon

Lemons are fairly new to the West, probably coming to us from Arabia or India. They were not known to the ancient Greeks or Romans. They reached Spain and North Africa around 1000–1200 AD. And the Crusaders found lemons growing in Palestine, and began bringing them back to Europe. The lemon was being commercially grown in the Azores by 1494, with most of them shipped to England.

Today, a commercial lemon tree can deliver about 1,500 lemons each year.

Lemon — Fact and Fable

The juice of the lemon is rich in vitamin C (50–60 mg per 100 g of raw lemon pulp) and quite acidic (pH 2–3, thanks to the citric acid).

However, some people claim that lemons will cure everything from leaking bile ducts and stomach ulcers to smallpox and AIDS, with appendicitis, cardiac palpitations and the common cold thrown in. As always, the ever popular 'sexual weakness' is on the list of potentially treatable woes.

And yes, also included on the list is the ability of lemons to magically dissolve away fats.

Lemon Juice Removes Mercury From Fish!

Nope, it doesn't.

It has been claimed that lemon juice could remove mercury from fish. It would supposedly release mercury from its bound state, allowing it to be wafted away on the wind once it had been converted to a volatile state. Unfortunately, the research by Dr J.N. Morgan and his colleagues at the National Exposure Research Laboratory of the US Environmental Protection Agency in Ohio showed that this did not happen.

But it would have been nice if it had . . .

The zInG PhAt InFo

There's no denying that lemon juice on fish adds zing,
but unfortunately there are no fat-fighting benefits
to be had from it.

The super-powered `LEMON`

A typical molecule of fat showing its structure.

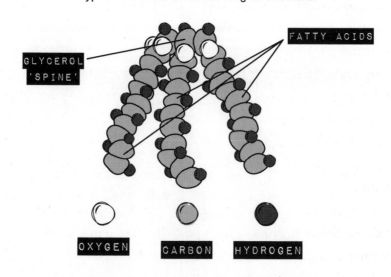

`GLYCEROL 'SPINE'`

`FATTY ACIDS`

`OXYGEN`   `CARBON`   `HYDROGEN`

According to biochemists, when a fat is broken down into its constituents, the 'ester bonds' are broken, leaving behind three fatty acids and one glycerol molecule. But to do this, you need either a strong hydroxide, or a strong hot acid. Lemon juice is an acid. It is easy to make your lemon juice hot — by using, for example an oven, a stove top, a microwave or a hot poker. But it is definitely not a strong acid. If you heat it up, you just get a hot, weak acid. Therefore, lemon juice simply cannot break down fats.

Twist in Myth

In fact, if the myth were true, and if lemon juice could break down fats, it would produce more kilojoules, not fewer. It would do this via two pathways — saving your body from having to burn kilojoules, and then enabling more kilojoules in your gut to cross into your bloodstream.

In the first case, under normal conditions, your body has to manufacture the strong internal acids that can break down fats. It takes many kilojoules of your metabolic energy to make these strong acids. These kilojoules are then subtracted from your daily total. But if lemon juice really did break down fats, you wouldn't have to make these strong stomach acids. If you didn't burn up extra kilojoules to make these strong stomach acids, you would have these extra kilojoules left over, and they would add to your waistline.

In the second case, just imagine that you have eaten a very fatty meal, and the fat is sitting in your gut. There are times when this fat does not end up on your waist. Suppose that you have eaten so much fat that you get a minor bout of diarrhoea. In this case, some of the fat exits at the other end into the toilet bowl — which means that it did not get into your bloodstream and then onto your waist. The medical name for this is 'steatorrhoea' — abnormally fatty stools which leave the fatty residue sometimes found in your toilet bowl.

But if lemon juice breaks down or dissolves the fat in food, the big collections of fat have turned into many smaller collections of fat — with a much larger surface area. The larger surface area means that they are more easily absorbed from the gut. Once you break down fats, the fatty acids and the glycerol do not magically vanish into a black hole, never to be seen again. No, they are still in your body, and are ultimately broken down into kilojoules which, once again, appear on your waistline.

If you really want to get rid of the obvious fat in meat, it's easy: get a knife and slice off the visible fat. And for fish, most of the fat comes from frying it in batter or crumbs. So get a fork and pick off the fatty batter or crumbs, or simply grill the fish.

Fat, Juicy Lemon Lie

So how did this myth start? Well, nobody really knows. Perhaps it arose because lemon juice has some useful properties. For example, lemon juice can break down the amines in fish into nonvolatile ammonium salts, so neutralising the fishy odour. And, second, the acid in lemon juice can hydrolise the tough fibres of collagen in meat, making it more tender. These are real properties of lemon juice.

Perhaps these real properties of lemon juice gave us this fat juicy lemon lie.

And there's no denying that a twist of lemon juice gives fish an extra zing. But as far as Fat-Fighting Properties go, someone has been squeezing more than the truth from the humble lemon …

Lemon Juice Fades Tattoos!

Sorry, but this is a lie. Lemon juice does not fade tattoos, even if you throw in some exposure to sunlight.

Dr Chapel and his colleagues tested this on rats that had been shaved and tattooed. Lemon juice plus sunlight made no difference to tattoos that were made with Indian ink.

References

Chapel, J.L., et al., 'Lemon juice, sunlight, and tattoos', *International Journal of Dermatology*, September 1983, Vol 22, Issue 7, pp 434–435.

Morgan, J.N., et al., 'Effects of commonly used cooking practices on total mercury concentration in fish and their impact on exposure assessments', *Journal of Exposure Analysis and Environmental Epidemiology*, Jan–March 1997, Vol 7, No 1, pp 119–133.

Red HAir Extinct

It seems the mere whiff of authority can turn something that is quite obviously silly and lacking credibility into something that people believe.

A good example is the erroneous claim that red (and blond) hair is caused by recessive genes, and will soon vanish from the human gene pool. For the same reason, blue eyes will also supposedly disappear.

Modern Myth

I first heard the myth a few years ago, when a substitute teacher at my daughter's high school told the class that blue eyes and red hair were carried by 'recessive' genes and, therefore, would soon vanish from the population. The mistake was the word 'therefore' — because recessive genes do not automatically vanish.

But the teacher was not deliberately trying to mislead the students. He was simply relating a story that newspapers and TV stations around the globe were carrying at the time. These media stories foretold the loss of red hair from the gene pool by 2202. A few of the stories mentioned that blond hair would also vanish. (Often they also reported that blue eyes would be lost from our descendants' gene pool, but this was usually buried deep in the story — the hair angle seemed to attract more attention from the journalists.)

The story had just enough scientific words thrown in (such as 'genome' and 'recessive genes') to give it some veracity. A dash of authority and integrity was added by quoting the World Health Organization and/or the seemingly prestigious Oxford Hair Foundation.

In truth, the whole story was a complete furphy. Many people in the news media were conned. But these people were conned only because they didn't check their facts.

Physics of Measurement

The news media around the world claimed that red and blond hair (and blue eyes) would be extinct by 2202.

This was a remarkably precise (and totally inaccurate) prediction. The original press release from the Oxford Hair Foundation quoted 'two centuries'. In scientific terms, the 'precision' is 'half the smallest unit'. In this case, the smallest unit is a 'century', so 'two centuries' means anywhere between 1.5 and 2.5 centuries.

The journalists who copied the press release received it in the year 2002. They saw 'two centuries' and added 200 years to get the year 2202. But in the case of the year '2202', the precision is half the smallest unit, which is a 'year'. So, saying that something will happen in 2202 means that it will happen between June/July 2201 and June/July 2203. What the press release originally implied (wrongly) was that the recessive genes would vanish from the gene pool somewhere between 2150 and 2350. (What's two centuries between friends, and especially with such a fuzzy measurement.)

Origin of Myth

The genetics behind this story about red hair and blue eyes began way back in the 18th century when Chinese and Japanese mouse breeders began crossbreeding mice with coats of different colours. They preferred certain colours (for purely aesthetic reasons) and tried to breed for these colours.

This stimulated more interest in genetics. As the mouse breeders quickly discovered, they didn't always get the colour they thought they were breeding for. Those simple experiments back then led to an inaccurate and shallow understanding of genetics — simply because genetics is actually very complicated (because 'life' is very complicated). Unfortunately, but understandably, this incomplete understanding led to inaccurate conclusions.

So, by 1865 the first documented mention of this myth (about red hair and blue eyes vanishing) appeared in an American journal, *The Flag of Our Union*. The myth never went away, popping up every decade or so in various US newspapers. It surfaced in the *Boston Daily Globe* in 1890, the *Marion Daily Star* in 1906 and, more recently, in the *Appleton Post-Crescent* in 1961.

A typical article, entitled 'Blondes to be Extinct', which ran in the *New Oxford Item*, a newspaper from New Oxford, Pennsylvania, on 7 March 1907, stated: '... But in about six hundred years the blonde will be a curiosity. She is to join the horse with five toes and the dodo ... It is based on the fact that blonds are growing scarcer and that the pigment in the skin which controls the colour of the face is an indication of the strength of the race. The dark haired persons will outlive the blonds, and marriage and commingling of types mean that the stronger will predominate ... The blond is of lower vitality than the brunette.'

The so-called 'science' behind the myth was always the

same—very simple, easy to understand, making perfect sense but, unfortunately, almost completely wrong.

Genetics 101

The myth began with a few, mostly correct, implied beliefs about genetics.

You have probably heard about 'genes'. Genes are the basic 'units of inheritance' that determine a particular characteristic that parents can pass on to their children, such as height or skin colour. And you might have heard of genes being 'dominant' or 'recessive'.

For example, think about the ear lobe, which is often decorated with earrings. Depending on the person, ear lobes can be either attached to the skin at the side of the head or float freely in the breeze. Suppose one parent has attached ear lobes, but the other has ear lobes that are free (or detached). Their offspring will usually have free ear lobes. So, in this case, we say that the gene for 'free ear lobes' is 'dominant', while the gene for 'attached ear lobes' is 'recessive'. Both parents must carry the gene for attached ear lobes for a child to have attached ear lobes.

However, even if both parents have free ear lobes, their children can still have attached ear lobes. For a child to have attached ear lobes, the two parents don't have to have attached ear lobes, they just each have to carry the recessive gene for attached ear lobes somewhere in their DNA. This is a good example of just how complicated genetics is.

Recessive genes do not have to automatically vanish. For example, about 1 in 25 white Caucasians carries the recessive gene for cystic fibrosis. Until recently, this disease used to lead to a very short life expectancy — and yet this recessive gene still survives. (See the 'Sports Drinks' chapter, p 42ff. In some cases, cystic fibrosis can provide some protection from the sometimes fatal diarrhoea of cholera.)

So recessive genes for red hair and blue eyes are not about to vanish — nor will red hair and blue eyes.

Genetics 999

Genes are complicated and, in the past, most high school biology books used to explain genes with simple examples relating to hair and eye colour. Unfortunately, these explanations were too simplistic. In fact, in some cases, they were wrong. For example, until recently, our understanding of how hair colour and eye colour passed from one generation to the next was deeply flawed.

Doctors Tom Ha and Jonathan L. Rees, from the Department of Dermatology at the University of Edinburgh, wrote: 'High school biology texts usually try to make genetics palatable by citing hair and eye colour traits as examples of the ways in which genes work. The fact that until comparatively recently we hadn't the faintest notion of the genetics of these traits seemed to receive little of the schoolmasters' attention. In truth, we still know little about eye colour, but we are beginning to understand certain hair colours, namely, red hair.'

It was only in the late 1990s that we found the first gene involved in red hair. But, as with everything in the human body, the inheritance of hair colour is very complicated. Factors that affect this inheritance include different pigment receptors on various cells, 'incomplete dominance with regard to different allele variants' and, of course, there could be other genes for red hair on other chromosomes.

Here are some other examples of just how complicated this topic is — we still don't know how a man can have a red beard and black hair, and we still don't know why hair changes colour during our lifetime. However, we are beginning to understand the molecular basis of why some animals have slightly different colours on their front and back.

We are also beginning to understand why red-haired women get very good pain relief from certain opiate painkillers (the k-opioids); they can get a longer lasting and more complete pain amelioration than dark-haired women. It turns out that the receptor gene involved in red hair (Melanocortin 1 Receptor, MC1R) is also involved in mediating pain relief from the k-opioids. However, we still do not understand why red-haired men do not experience the same pain relief.

Red Hair in Culture

The most recognised redhead in the USA is Ariel, Disney's Little Mermaid.
In Scotland, 13% of the population has red hair.

Get the Facts

The story of blonds and redheads becoming extinct is still resurfacing in the media, and journalists are still not checking the facts.

If they did, they would have found that the World Health Organization (WHO) had categorically denied having anything to do with this story. The official WHO rebuttal, entitled 'Clarification of erroneous news reports indicating WHO genetic research on hair colour', stated: 'Nor has WHO issued a report predicting that natural blondes are likely to be extinct by 2202. WHO has no knowledge of how these news reports originated but would like to stress that we have no opinion on the future existence of blondes.'

Red-y, Set, Gone

(due to printing constraints, red appears as grey)

The generalised (mis)understanding is that because
red hair is caused by a recessive gene,
redheads will soon vanish from existence.

ANOTHER EXAMPLE OF RECESSIVE GENES

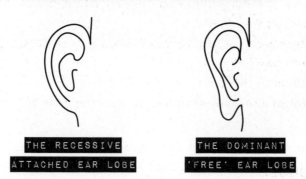

THE RECESSIVE
ATTACHED EAR LOBE

THE DOMINANT
'FREE' EAR LOBE

The ear lobe look can have two major possibilities –
it can be attached to the skin at the side of your head,
or it can float freely.

It took only a few clicks of the mouse for me to find this on the WHO home page.

And if the journalists had simply tried to look up the home page of the Oxford Hair Foundation, they would have found it is almost totally devoid of content. It reads: 'The Oxford Hair Foundation website has decided to transfer its information to P & G Beauty Science instead. Thank you for your visit.' Hopefully, this myth will follow the example of the Oxford Hair Foundation and vanish as well. The mighty and impressive 'Oxford Hair Foundation' was just a media outlet for a hair company — albeit a media outlet with a very fancy name.

Perhaps this 'blond-scientific' study is less of a bombshell and more an empty shell of a story. And perhaps the media still runs with the old adage of 'Never let the truth stand in the way of a good story'.

My Aimed-for Writing Ethics

1   Never print anything as a direct quote when it comes from a press release.
2   Give readers enough accurate information to make their own judgments.
3   Research the story properly.
4   Always admit my mistakes quickly and openly.

References

Altman, Lawrence K., 'Stop those presses! Blonds, it seems, will survive after all', *The New York Times*, 2 October 2002.

Duffy, David L., et al., 'A three–single-nucleotide polymorphism haplotype in intron 1 of *OCA2* explains most human eye-colour variation', *The American Journal of Human Genetics*, February 2007, Vol 80, No 2, pp 241–252.

'Extinction of blondes vastly overreported: media fail to check root of "study"', *Washington Post*, 2 October 2002.

Ha, Tom, and Rees, Jonathan L., 'Melanocortin 1 receptor: what's red got to do with it?' *Journal of the American Academy of Dermatology*, 2001, Vol 45, No 6, pp 961–964.

Henig, Robin Marantz, 'The genome in black and white (and gray)', *The New York Times*, 10 October 2004.

Mogil, Jeffrey S., et al., 'The melanocortin-1 receptor gene mediates female-specific mechanisms of analgesia in mice and humans', *Proceedings of the National Academy of Science* (PNAS), 15 April 2003, Vol 100, No 8, pp 4867–4872.

Rees, Jonathan L., 'The melanocortin 1 receptor (MC1R): more than just red hair', *Pigment Cell Research*, 2000, Vol 13, pp 135–140.

Seven-Year Regrowth

(A myth in its prime)

The number seven has long had special significance in our culture. For example, there are seven days in the week; the seven deadly sins are counterbalanced by the seven virtues; there are also the seven wonders of the world; and ancient astronomers identified and named seven planets. Even today, motivational books will often use the number seven in the title, e.g. *The Seven Habits of Highly Effective People*, *The Seven Principles for Making Marriage Work* and *The Seven Pillars of Health*.

But the number seven's other Special Claim to Fame is the very widely held belief that our bodies are renewed every seven years. This claim comes from many sources including new-age therapies, beauty products, health foods and motivational speakers. This sevenish Claim to Fame has also been linked to the incorrect assertion that women's bodies have a major hormonal shift every seven years.

However, new research has finally been able to measure the life span of various human cells in different body organs. And, in doing so, it has exposed the simple lie of the seven-year renewal of the human body.

se7en Is (not) the MAGIC Number

There is a widely held belief that our bodies are renewed every seven years. BUT, the research of scientists has told us that cells in different parts of the body get renewed at different rates.

REPLACE GUT LINING

REPLACE SKIN CELLS

RED BLOOD CELLS

LIVER

BONE REBUILD

MUSCLE CELLS

On average, most of your body is less than 10 years old – probably around 5.6 years.

How Old Are You?

This new research is helping us answer the age-old question: How old are you? In actual fact, this is a very difficult question to answer. You see, this new research tells us that we are all older than our bodies — if we start the clock ticking when we are born.

There are many mysteries about ageing. For example, why do human beings live so much longer than most other mammals? Why does our memory fade as we get older? How does our brain remember things?

And there is yet another mystery. At what rate do different parts of the human body renew or replicate themselves?

The key to solving the renewal-rate mystery involves a simple fact, which is that every living creature on Earth takes in carbon from its environment.

Carbon from the atmosphere reacts with oxygen to form carbon dioxide. This carbon dioxide can then enter plants via photosynthesis. Animals, including human beings, then consume these plants.

At 18.5%, carbon is the second most common element (by mass) in the human body, after oxygen.

Radioactive Carbon 101

Carbon atoms come in a few different varieties or 'isotopes'. Practically all of the carbon that occurs in the biosphere consists of the non-radioactive isotope carbon-12 (C-12). But if you look very carefully, you will find that for every million million (trillion) atoms of carbon-12, there is one atom of radioactive carbon-14 (C-14).

C-14 is continually being made naturally, whenever a neutron associated with a cosmic ray from Outer Space slams into a

Carbon-14

Carbon is the sixth lightest element, so it has – in its core or nucleus – six protons. An isotope (of any element) has the same number of protons, but a variable number of neutrons. Carbon has approximately 15 isotopes, most of them extremely rare and uncommon.

A carbon nucleus with six neutrons is the isotope carbon-12, which accounts for about 99% of the carbon found in the biosphere. This isotope is not radioactive.

A carbon nucleus with seven neutrons is the isotope carbon-13, which accounts for about 1% of carbon. This isotope is also not radioactive.

A nucleus with eight neutrons is the isotope carbon-14, and accounts for about a one-trillionth part of carbon. Carbon-14 is radioactive.

Carbon-14 was discovered during World War II, on 27 February 1940, at the University of California Radiation Laboratory in Berkeley. Its discoverers were Martin Kamen and Sam Ruben.

nitrogen atom. Nitrogen makes up about 80% of our atmosphere — the stuff that we breathe. So there's lots of nitrogen available to be hit by cosmic rays. (In the following equation, 'n' is a neutron, while 'p' is a proton. Cosmic rays provide the energy to 'pump up' a nitrogen atom into a radioactive carbon atom.)

$$n + {}^{14}_{7}N \rightarrow {}^{14}_{6}C + p$$

Being radioactive, C-14 also decays naturally, with a half-life of about 5,730 years. It decays back to stable, non-radioactive nitrogen. (In the following equation, 'e⁻' is an electron, while 'V̄ₑ' is an electron antineutrino.)

$$^{14}_{6}C \rightarrow {}^{14}_{7}N + e^- + \bar{V}_e$$

For billions of years there has been a balance between C-14's natural production and its natural decay. This balance gave the environment low (and fairly constant) background levels of C-14. (As mentioned above, there is about one atom of C-14 for every trillion atoms of 'regular' C-12.)

The C-14 level in the atmosphere mirrors fairly closely the C-14 levels in living creatures (because we are always taking in and excreting — to put it politely — carbon).

So all living creatures take in some kind of food from the environment — and this food always has some carbon in it. But of course, once an animal dies, it stops eating. It no longer takes up any carbon and, consequently, no more C-14. So once it dies, its levels of C-14 halve every 5,730 years. This concept is used in the technique called radiocarbon dating in archaeology to determine the age of material remains that were once living, e.g. trees and animals.

However, in the 1940s, human beings invented nuclear weapons. When nukes explode, they also make C-14. So our nuclear weapons added extra C-14 into the atmosphere. By 1963, when the testing of nuclear weapons in the atmosphere was stopped thanks to the Partial Test Ban Treaty, the background levels of C-14 in living creatures had already doubled (to about two atoms of C-14 for every trillion atoms of 'regular' C-12).

The scientists realised that this short-lived 'spike' of radioactive C-14 from nuclear weapons could be used as a 'clock' to measure cell life — and that led to the big breakthrough for this new research on cell and tissue dating.

Your Food is Radioactive

All the food you eat is – very slightly – radioactive. That's because out of every trillion atoms of carbon, just one is the radioactive carbon-14.

Half-Life

The 'half-life' of a radioactive element is the time taken for half of the atoms to decay into another element. The term was first used in 1907 and, at the time, was known as a 'half-life period'. But the word 'period' was dropped in the early 1950s, and today we just call it a 'half-life'.

For example, radon-222 has a half-life of less than four days, while uranium-238 (not the isotope that goes 'bang') has a half-life of 4.47 billion years. It's 704 million years for uranium-235 (the isotope that does go 'bang').

At the short end of half-lives is carbon-8. It has a half-life of about two-thousandths of a billionth of a billionth of a second.

Carbon-14 has a half-life of 5,730 years.

Suppose we have a million atoms of C-14. We know that after about 5,730 years, we will have only half a million atoms of C-14 (the rest will have decayed back to nitrogen). After a further 5,730 years, we will be left with only 250,000 atoms of C-14. And so on.

Or to express a half-life in another way, if you have a gram of carbon (with all the carbon isotopes in their respective proportions), in each second there will be just 14 disintegrations or decays of C-14 atoms.

Now here's something really weird about the half-life of an element and radioactive decay.

We have no way of telling *which* individual atoms will decay. We also have no way of telling *when* (in that 5,730-year window) any of those atoms will decay.

Radioactive decay is totally random – one of the very few events in our Universe that is.

The Age of Your Brain

By the way, in the cells in your body, most of the molecules are in a state of constant flux and exchange with the environment. One unique exception is your DNA — this interacts with the environment only when it divides. So the C-14 levels in DNA can be used to establish the birth date of the cells that the DNA belongs to.

Dr Jonas Frisen from Sweden and Dr David Fink from the Australian Nuclear Science and Technology Organisation (ANSTO) were among the authors of the paper 'Neocortical neurogenesis in humans is restricted to development'. Dr Fink and his team used an ultra-sensitive technique called Accelerator Mass Spectrometry to count the number of C-14 atoms in the DNA in neurons from human brain cells. This allowed Dr Fink to test samples as small as ten-millionths of a gram. This corresponds to the DNA from as few as five million cells.

The numbers are quite astonishing. In the DNA of a single cell, there are about 64 billion carbon atoms. But you have to look at one thousand billion carbon atoms to find a single C-14 atom. This means you need to look at the DNA of 15 cells to find just one C-14 atom. And we can do this — aren't human beings wonderful!

Their amazing discovery was that the neurons (or nerve cells) in most of your brain are as old as you are. It makes sense that the nerves in your vision and memory centres preserve, for your whole life, the knowledge of how you see and how you remember.

But the cells in your cerebellum — which are concerned with balance and coordination — are about 2.9 years younger than you. This also makes sense, as balance and coordination develop during the years of infancy.

However, in the brain, there are cells that are not nerve cells — these are called glial cells. They are about ten times as common as nerve cells, with some people believing that glial cells act as 'support' or 'supply' cells for the neurons. (On the other hand, Albert Einstein had an abnormally high percentage of glial cells.) On average, you have about 100 billion glial cells in your brain, but only ten billion neurons. Anyhow, glial cells are 4.9 years younger than your birth age.

Brain Cells Do (Not) Replace?

When I went to medical school (in the 1980s), we were taught that brain cells *never* repair themselves and *never* replicate.

Today, it is quite well established that some brain cells in some parts of the brain *do* replicate. These regions include the hippocampus and the area around the ventricles. This replication happens throughout life in all the mammals that have been studied. But most of the human brain does not replicate.

However, there is continuing neurogenesis (growth of new nerve cells) in large areas of the brains of many non-humans, such as fish, zebra finches, canaries, frogs and reptiles.

Why has this ability been lost in human beings? We don't know, but it might be to ensure the preservation of memories.

So perhaps the permanent loss of neurons due to stroke, infection, trauma, ageing and degeneration is part of the price that we have to pay for being human.

The Many Ages of Man

The research of other scientists tells us that cells in different parts of the body become renewed at different rates.

Your gut runs approximately 10 m from your mouth to your anus. The cells that line the gut are replaced every five days. On the other hand, the cells in the gut that are not part of the lining get replaced every 15.9 years.

The turnover time for skin cells is about two weeks. Red blood cells are recycled every 120 days, while muscle cells hang around for 15.1 years. Bone is rebuilt every ten years. The liver is about two years old.

The enamel in your teeth is laid down at certain and well-defined times in your childhood. The enamel consists of 0.4% carbon. This carbon is never replaced, making teeth a 'clock' which is accurate to 1.6 years.

On average, most of your body is less than ten years old — probably around 5.6 years. But your rate of growing new neurons drops if you suffer from depression or dementia — these are other factors that change your 'body age'.

Your brain is older than the rest of your body. So you can definitely say that 'you' (i.e. the body you are wearing today) have not been around since 'you' (the consciousness) were born — it all depends on your definition of 'you'.

So back to the question of how old you are. First, let's say that the person that is 'you' is the consciousness that makes you different from every other person on the planet. Now 'you' have a body. That body is made up of several hundred different types of cells (e.g. in your liver, lung and heart). The vast majority of those cells have a life span considerably shorter than the life span of your consciousness.

We still don't know how 'old' you are, and how many 'bodies' you use up in your lifetime — but we do know that the bland claim that your cells are replaced every seven years is as wrong as the claim that a cat has nine lives.

C-14 Not Constant? Inaccurate?

Unfortunately, the C-14 levels are not the same everywhere in the atmosphere and, even trickier, not the same at all times.

C-14 is not the same everywhere in the atmosphere? Nope. First, the Earth's magnetic field is most effective at blocking incoming radiation at the Equator, and weakest at the North and South Poles. So cosmic rays are weakest at the Equator, and strongest at the poles. As a result, most of the C-14 is made in the atmosphere near the poles, at altitudes of 9–15 km (30,000–50,000 ft). However, given enough time, the heat of the Sun stirs the atmosphere quite well, and spreads the C-14 quite evenly across the planet.

C-14 is not the same at all times? The cosmic ray activity varies with time due to, for example, changes in the Earth's magnetic fields.

In addition, old carbon (such as coal, natural gas and oil, resources that have been underground for millions of years) has lost practically all of its C-14, due to radioactive decay. When we take this old carbon (which is deficient in C-14) out of the ground and burn it, this carbon (now in carbon dioxide) enters the atmosphere and lowers the levels of C-14. Volcanoes can erupt lots of carbon low in C-14 into the environment, thus lowering the local concentration of C-14. If it's a small eruption it's just a local effect, but if it's an enormous eruption it can affect the atmosphere of the entire Earth.

But working in the other direction, the atmospheric testing of nuclear weapons raised the C-14 levels in the atmosphere.

Marine uptake of carbon can change with time, either up or down.

However, by making C-14 measurements in many different situations, and comparing the C-14 dates to the dates taken by (say) measuring tree rings, we can apply various corrections. (This field of study is called 'dendrochronology', and we have continuous records to about 11,000 years ago that can be linked directly with radiocarbon dating.) We can also cross-link radiocarbon dating with deposits from caves, going back 45,000 years.

Radiocarbon dating requires skill and knowledge. When these are applied, it can give us dates back to 60,000 years or so, with an accuracy of a few per cent. After about 60,000 years, there are not enough C-14 atoms left to be useful for radiocarbon dating.

References

Nowakowski, Richard S., 'Stable neuron numbers from cradle to grave', *Proceedings of the National Academy of Sciences* (PNAS), 15 August 2006, Vol 103, No 33, pp 12219–12220.

Rakic, Pasko, 'No more cortical neurons for you', *Science*, 18 August 2006, Vol 313, No 5789, pp 928, 929.

Spalding, Kirsty L., et al., 'Forensics: age written in teeth by nuclear tests', *Nature*, 15 September 2005, pp 333, 334.

Spalding, Kirsty L., et al., 'Retrospective birth dating of cells in humans', *Cell*, 15 July 2005, Vol 122, Issue 1, pp 133–143.

Vince, Gaia, 'The many ages of man', *New Scientist*, 17 June 2006, pp 50–53.

zero Gravity in Space?

(Don't FALL For It!)

The first human being to fly in Space was the Russian cosmonaut Yuri Gagarin, on 12 April 1961. Since then, we have all seen TV and movie footage of astronauts floating both inside, and outside, their spacecraft — seemingly unaffected by gravity. But despite what the journalists tell us, these astronauts are not in zero gravity.

There Ain't No Zero

The astronauts in orbit are *not* in 'zero gravity'.

Nope, the gravity of every object (no matter how little mass it has) reaches to the very edges of the Universe.

The gravitational field becomes weaker as it gets further away, but it never drops to zero.

As a result, every location in the Universe is filled with squillions of individual gravitational fields, each generated by the squillions of individual objects in the Universe, such as giant stars, small asteroids, and even the pen in my shirt pocket. At any location, these gravitational fields can combine to make a bigger gravitational field, or cancel to make a smaller one. It would be almost impossible to find a location in the Universe where the gravitational fields all cancel out to be exactly zero.

Astronaut? In Space?

Space travellers from Western countries are called 'astronauts'. Those from Russia are called 'cosmonauts', while those from China are called 'taikonauts'. In all of these words, the 'naut' part comes from the Greek word *nautes* meaning 'sailor', while both 'astro' and 'cosmo' refer to 'star'. The 'taik' in 'taikonaut' comes from the Chinese word *taikong* meaning 'Space'.

Originally, all Space travellers were sent up into Space by government agencies. But commercial Space flight began in 2004 with the launch of the privately funded spacecraft called *SpaceShipOne*.

The definition of 'Space' varies. The FAI (Fédération Aéronautique Internationale) Sporting Code for astronautics recognises Space flights only as those that exceed the arbitrary altitude of 100 km above the surface of the Earth. But the USA awards Astronaut Wings to those who have reached above 80 km.

Sergei K. Krikalev holds the male record for time spent in Space (2.2 years, or 803 days, 9 hours and 39 minutes), while Peggy A. Whitson holds the female record (1.03 years, or 377 days).

However, in the spaces between the galaxies, millions of light years from each other, the gravity would be pretty close to zero.

But that's not the case with astronauts orbiting the Earth.

Construction of the International Space Station (ISS) began in 1998. It has been orbiting the Earth, with astronauts continually on board, since 2 November 2000. Its height varies between 330 and 410 km above the surface of the Earth. At this altitude, the 'atmosphere' is very thin, but the ISS is large and moves at around 25,000 kph. Atmospheric drag makes it lose about 200 m of altitude every day, so it has to be rebooted every 10–45 days.

The ISS is not far from Earth — you could cover this distance on a German autobahn in a few hours.

Gravity Not Constant Off Earth

The acceleration that gravity gives to a falling body weakens with altitude above the ground.

Ground, 0 km	100%
Top of Mt Everest, 8.8 km	99.7%
Space Shuttle Lowest Orbit, 250 km	92.6%
Space Shuttle Highest Orbit, 400 km	88.62%
Geostationary Communications Satellite, 36,000 km	0.02%

90% of Normal 'Weight'

The Earth has a radius of about 6,400 km. (It's actually 6,378.1 km at the Equator, and 6,356.8 km at the North and South Poles.) So the ISS is actually very close to the Earth — it's only about 5% of the radius away.

Isaac Newton told us, and he was right, that there is a gravitational attraction between any two bodies. The mathematicians tell us that you can think of all of the mass of the Earth as being concentrated at the centre. So when you stand on the surface, about 6,400 km away from the centre, your weight is (let's say) 80 kg.

Now, let's put you on the very top of a Giant Pin — about 350 km high. This is a great height, but it's only a pimple on the Earth, measuring only about 5% of its radius. I have chosen 350 km because this is the height at which the ISS and the space shuttles orbit. Gravity gets weaker as you move further away from its source.

Plug this extra distance into Newton's Equation of Gravity, and you find that you now weigh only 72 kg, about 10% less.

Please note — that's not 100% less, only 10% less.

So if the astronauts were standing on a weighing scale, on top of a Giant Pin 350 km high, they would weigh 90% of their normal weight.

Gravity Not Constant On Earth

There are many ways to measure the strength of the Earth's gravity. One very easy method is to see what acceleration our gravity gives to a freely falling object. This acceleration, called 'g', is often rounded off to 9.8 m/sec^2, i.e. with each passing second, the velocity of the falling object will increase by 9.8 m/sec.

It's higher at the North and South Poles, and lower at the Equator, for two different reasons.

First, it's higher at the poles because they are closer to the centre of the Earth than the Equator. This happens because the Earth spins, making the planet bulge outwards at the Equator. The closer distance makes the gravity stronger at the poles.

Second, it's weaker at the Equator, because the Earth spins on its own axis, generating an outward 'centrifugal force'. This 'outwards force' slightly weakens the inward 'suck' of gravity. So, again, gravity is stronger at the poles.

Adding these two factors together, 'g' is 9.832 m/sec^2 at the poles, and 9.782 m/sec^2 at the Equator.

How Come They Float?

So how come the astronauts float, if they still weigh 90% of their normal weight?

Simple: (1) they are falling because they have weight; but (2) they are moving forward really really quickly; and (3) the Earth is curved, not flat.

Let me explain this to you.

First, the astronauts are so close to the Earth that the Earth's gravitational field 'sucks' on them with 90% of its normal 'suck'. So they do actually fall towards the Earth. At ground level, if you jumped off a diving board into a pool, you would fall 5 m in the first second. But the Earth's gravity is a little weaker at their altitude of about 350 km, so they fall 4.5 m in the first second. And yes, they really do fall.

Second, at their altitude, they are also moving forward at about 25,000 kph — in other words, 7 km in each second.

Third, the Earth is not flat — it has the shape of a ball, with a curved surface. At the astronauts' altitude, the curve of the Earth drops away by roughly 4.5 m for every 7 km that they fly forward.

Therefore in the exact second that they move forward 7 km, gravity pulls them 4.5 m vertically downwards towards the Earth. But (as I said earlier) in the 7 km that they cover in that second, the curve of the Earth is such that the surface of our planet has 'fallen' away by 4.5 m.

Free Fall

For our astronauts, the net result is simple. After one second of falling, they are still the same distance from the surface of the Earth.

And so it goes for every single second that they are in orbit at that particular speed and altitude. After 90 minutes, they have made a complete loop of the Earth and are still the same distance from the surface.

In one second, the shuttle moves forward 7 kilometres, while at the same time, gravity pulls it 4.5 metres vertically downwards towards the Earth. But in the 7 kilometres it covers in that second, the curve of the Earth is such that the surface of our planet has 'fallen' away by 4.5 metres.

At the altitude of 350 km, the path of the shuttle drops away by roughly 4.5 m for every 7 km it flies forward

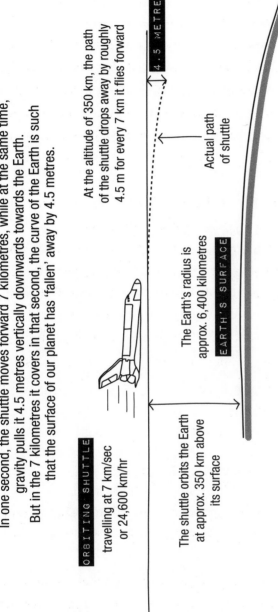

4.5 METRES

Actual path of shuttle

ORBITING SHUTTLE

travelling at 7 km/sec or 24,600 km/hr

The Earth's radius is approx. 6,400 kilometres

EARTH'S SURFACE

The shuttle orbits the Earth at approx. 350 km above its surface

For our astronauts, the net result is simple – free fall. After one second of falling, they are still the same distance from the surface of the Earth.

why zero AIN'T rEALLY zERO

They are in 'free fall'. They are always falling freely — but thanks to the perfect matching of their speed and the curve of the Earth, they are always the same distance from the surface of the Earth.

A few centuries ago, Isaac Newton considered this problem of 'free fall' by what scientists call a Thought Experiment. He thought about a cannon mounted (say) 1 m above the ground. If it had a small charge of gunpowder, the ball would fly 100 m before gravity pulled it down and it hit the ground. A bigger charge would make it fly 100 km before it hit the ground. An absolutely huge charge

Vomit Comet

The 'Vomit Comet' was the name given to the aeroplanes operated by the NASA Reduced Gravity Research Foundation. By flying in a series of up-and-down curves, each about 10 km long, the pilots can generate about 25 seconds of effective weightlessness for every 65 seconds of flight. Of course, there's no such thing as a free lunch, so the 25 seconds of weightlessness are balanced by a similar period of double gravity.

The name Vomit Comet arose because, under these trying conditions, about one-third of passengers vomited a lot, about one-third were just nauseated and felt like vomiting, and about one-third were unaffected.

The first NASA Vomit Comet was a Lockheed C-131. After its retirement from service in 1959, it was replaced by two KC-135 Stratotankers. One, NASA 930, was used to film weightlessness sequences for the movie *Apollo 13*.

Today, several commercial operators now offer the sensation of weightlessness.

In 2005, NASA began using a C-9B Skytrain II. And NASA renamed it with the 'nicer' nickname of 'Weightless Wonder' rather than 'Vomit Comet'.

would make it fly 1 m above the ground all the way around the Earth (assuming that there was no wind resistance). If there were no wind resistance, the cannonball would orbit the Earth forever.

So, like the astronauts, the cannonball would always be falling. But, again, there's the perfect match of its speed and the curve of the Earth. So it's always falling toward the Earth, and the surface of the Earth is always dipping away from it.

'Weightless'

Suppose you are standing on your bathroom scales. Gravity pulls you down onto the scales. The scales are, in turn, resting on the bathroom floor. They 'push' back up, allowing you to register a certain weight on your scales.

Now, let's try this experiment but in a different location. There are several 'Free Fall Facilities' around the planet. NASA has the Zero Gravity Research Facility at the Glenn Research Center in Cleveland, Ohio with a 145 m vertical shaft, in which an experiment can fall 132 m in 5.18 seconds. Suppose you stand on your bathroom scales on a trapdoor at the top of the vertical shaft. Your weight is (say) 80 kg. The scales register 80 kg. Then the trapdoor opens, and you and the scales (still touching each other) begin to fall. Gravity still pulls on you (which is why you fall). Your feet press on the scales. But the scales don't press back, because they are not resting on the floor. So the scales register no weight — and you are now 'weightless'.

You are now in free fall (just like the astronauts). Unfortunately, you don't have a horizontal velocity of 7 km/sec. So after a few seconds you slam into the 4.5 m thick pile of expanded polystyrene pellets at the bottom of the shaft and come to a very painful halt.

We can experience a kind of free fall down here on Earth, but only for brief instances.

Free Fall on Earth

According to the *Guinness Book of Records*, the longest free fall on Earth happened to Vesna Vulovic, a flight attendant with JAT Airlines on 26 January 1972. Her aeroplane, a DC-9, exploded thanks to a bomb planted by the Ustashe (the Croatian National Movement). The DC-9, Flight JAT 367, was en route from Copenhagen to Zagreb and Belgrade.

The DC-9 broke into pieces, and Vesna fell more than 33,000 ft (10,000 m). Vesna lost all memory from one hour before the explosion to one month afterwards. She fractured her skull, suffered a brain haemorrhage and fractured three spinal vertebrae. She was initially paralysed from the waist down, but after an operation and a few months recovery, could walk again. She received her Guinness Award in London from Paul McCartney, the ex-Beatle.

But her 'flight' was not a true free fall. Luckily, the air resisted her fall, limiting her top speed to about 200 kph.

And the free fall of Joseph Kittinger from 102,800 ft (31.3 km) was not a true free fall. He wore a multi-stage Beaupre Parachute that opened in three stages. Its purpose was to stabilise the high-altitude parachutist, and stop him from spinning and tumbling. The first mini-parachute (18 inches or 0.5 m across) deployed within a few seconds. In turn, this pulled out a small 6 ft (2 m) drogue parachute. Finally, at an altitude of around 14,000 ft (4.2 km), the 28 ft (8.5 m) parachute would deploy fully.

In his first test jump from a high-altitude balloon on 16 November 1959, the main parachute wrapped around his neck. Amazingly, he survived his fall from 76,400 ft (23.3 km). On his second test jump on 11 December 1959, he stepped out of the gondola of his balloon at 74,700 ft (22.8 km). There were no complications. His third and final jump was on 16 August 1960. Falling from 102,800 ft (31.3 km), he experienced temperatures as low as −70°C, and speeds up to around 1,000 kph. He fell in conditions close to free fall for 4 minutes and 36 seconds. The main parachute opened in the thicker atmosphere below 18,000 ft (5.4 km). The total fall time was 13 minutes and 45 seconds.

Joseph Kittinger, like Vesna Vulovic, was not in true free fall, as wind resistance slowed him down. He also had extra retardation from the small, stabilising drogue parachute.

Douglas Adams (in his book *Life, the Universe and Everything*) said that flying was quite easy — 'the knack lies in learning how to throw yourself at the ground and miss'. This is what the astronauts in space do — they continually fall towards the ground, and they continually miss it. It's not 'zero gravity' that keeps them up there — it's the combination of their massive horizontal speed and the curvature of the Earth.

NASA used to talk of 'zero gravity'. Today, they talk of 'microgravity'. Perhaps the correct approach is to realise that there is no such thing as gravity and, although the Earth may be a beautiful place, Earth's gravity really sucks …

Zero Gravity? Moon?

The Moon is a lot further away than the astronauts on the International Space Station, so does the Earth's gravity still affect it?

The Moon orbits the Earth at a distance of about 400,000 km. It continues to orbit the Earth because Earth's gravity is strong enough – even at a distance of 400,000 km – to hang onto it.

So if the Earth's gravity can hang onto the Moon, it can easily hang onto astronauts a mere 350 km away.

References

McCallum, Yoka, et al., *Physics 2 HSC Course*, John Wiley & Sons, 2001, pp 2–12.

Young, Hugh D. and Freedman, Roger A., *University Physics with Modern Physics*, 11th edition, Pearson Education, 2004, pp 58-59, 166-167, 459-461.

Drugs Ain't Drugs

Antibiotics have been part of our lives since the end of World War II. Since then, the pharmacological armamentarium of modern medicine has grown in leaps and bounds. I love having access to antibiotics, and would hate to live in a world without them. On the other hand, I know that medications often have to be 'fine-tuned' to the individual patient.

Even so, I was quite surprised to read the statement of Dr Allen D. Roses in which he said, 'The vast majority of drugs — more than 90% — only work in 30 or 50% of the people.' He went on to clarify his statement: 'I wouldn't say that most drugs don't work. I would say that most drugs work in 30–50% of people. Drugs out there on the market work, but they don't work in everybody.'

At the time (December 2003), Dr Roses was worldwide vice-president of genetics at GlaxoSmithKline (GSK). Since then he has taken up a position at the Deane Drug Discovery Unit at the Duke University Medical Center in North Carolina in the USA.

Drugs Not Perfect

Here is a list of how effectively (percentage of cases) some conditions can be treated by medications:

Alzheimer's Disease	30%
Asthma	60%
Cardiac Arrhythmia	60%
Depression	62%
Diabetes	57%
Hepatitis C	47%
Migraine (acute)	52%
Migraine (prevention)	50%
Oncology (cancer)	25%
Rheumatoid Arthritis	50%
Schizophrenia	60%

There are plenty of good reasons why this success rate is so often way below 100%.

First, nothing that human beings have ever made is perfect. While we have been practising pharmacology for thousands of years, our modern pharmacology industry is barely half a century old, and human DNA was mapped only in the 21st century.

Second, the process by which new drugs are developed is not perfect. Typically, it takes about 15 years and $500 million to get a drug to the stage that it can be tested first on animals. These animals have been chosen to be genetically the same as each other. The drug is then tested on a relatively small group of human beings — who are each genetically different from each other. Drug toxicity at this final stage means that 90% of all drugs being developed get sidelined, never to be used. Finally, the drug is released onto the market, with careful monitoring in place to look for further side effects in the greater population.

Third, even though some of these conditions (e.g. asthma and schizophrenia) might have just a single name, the names actually cover many different conditions with different causes. The reason the different conditions have one name is that the final symptoms are very similar, e.g. shortness of breath in asthma or the inability

so MANy drugs, so Few Get through

90% of newly developed drugs are sidelined because they are toxic to a tiny percentage of the population. In the future, we hope to be able to use those drugs only on the 99.99% of people who can benefit from them, and steer these drugs away from the 0.01% of people to whom they are toxic.

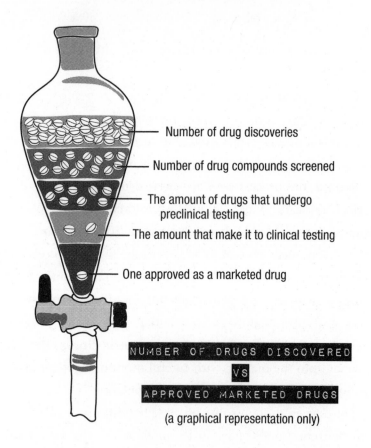

— Number of drug discoveries

— Number of drug compounds screened

— The amount of drugs that undergo preclinical testing

— The amount that make it to clinical testing

— One approved as a marketed drug

NUMBER OF DRUGS DISCOVERED
VS
APPROVED MARKETED DRUGS

(a graphical representation only)

to be oriented in time, place and person in schizophrenia. If these different diseases have different causes, they could easily require different treatments.

Fourth, there are so many environmental variables in people that affect medications — factors such as age, gender, tobacco use, exercise regime, diet, other medications that may interact, and so on.

Fifth, and probably most importantly, there are genetic factors involved. For example, how the drug enters the circulation, how it

Gattaca in US Military

Genetic discrimination is the theme of the movie *Gattaca*. The letters that make up the name 'Gattaca' are the initial letters of the four bases (or chemical compounds) that make up the human DNA – Adenine, Cytosine, Guanine and Thymine.

Genetic discrimination is now forbidden in the USA, thanks to the passing of the *Genetic Information Nondiscrimination Act* of 2008. The Act 'bars insurers from using the results from genetic tests to deny coverage to new applicants, or from hiking the price of premiums for existing customers. It would also make it illegal for employers to use genetic information in hiring, firing or promotion decisions.' (Of course, this Act has no relevance in Australia, it applies solely to the USA.)

But personnel of the US military are shamefully excluded from this protection. The medical cost would not be great. About 250 US military personnel are discharged each year for medical problems that have a genetic basis, the associated cost is estimated at $1.7 million annually. It is certainly very small, when compared to the estimated cost of $600 million per day for the Iraq War, a war that began on 20 March 2003.

is transported, how it is distributed around the body and how it works at the desired site of action.

Medical doctors (the people who prescribe the drugs developed by the pharmacologists) have long known that medications are not perfect. Often, doctors will have to carefully 'juggle' the medications of a patient to get the best results. Another consideration is that some patients will respond quite badly, and might even suffer life-threatening complications, despite having only a very small dose of a particular medication. This rare but very serious uncertainty (which is related to allergic response) is difficult to predict.

Opiate Variability

Opiates are a good example of a class of drug whose levels have to be juggled. Human beings have used opiates to relieve pain for many thousands of years. Today, besides the original drug opium, the opiate family includes morphine, codeine, oxycodone and heroin.

At any given moment, there are ten million people taking opiates for pain relief from cancer — indeed, 80% of people with advanced cancer experience great pain. But opiates are also administered for non-cancer-related pain, e.g. chronic pain and postoperative acute pain.

Opiates are generally good at relieving pain — but they are not perfect.

First, there is a relatively narrow margin between the dose that relieves pain and the dose that kills you via respiratory depression.

Second, there is enormous human variation in the dose needed to relieve pain. In one study of 3,000 people having hip-replacement surgery, the dose of opiate needed to provide adequate pain relief varied by a factor of 40 to 1. This variability is astonishingly large.

Many factors control this variation in the amount of pain relief in response to a given dose of opiate. These factors are also responsible for the variability in undesirable side effects.

In 15% of people the target site for the opiates varies, thus providing poor pain relief.

My Genes and Morphine

A few years ago, I had an accident with my 9 ft 6 in (2.9 m) surfboard. A wave smashed it into my left shoulder. (Never let your board get between you and a wave.) The 'ball' on my upper arm bone that fits into the 'socket' of my shoulder was smashed into about 40 pieces of rubble. Amazingly, the ball stayed intact, held together by clotting blood. The pain was so great that I didn't really feel any pain – I was totally dissociated from my body.

It's a Bad Sign in a hospital when staff start calling each other over to have a look at your X-ray. It's even worse when they start whistling in astonishment, and then poke a curious head through the curtains to see just what you look like. After more than an hour in the Emergency Room cubicle, and half-a-dozen staff checking me out, the pain in my shoulder began to build up.

The doctor offered me morphine for the pain, and I said yes. He warned me that it might cause nausea and vomiting, and gave me a drug to suppress these unpleasant side effects of nausea and vomiting. Then he gave me the morphine.

I spent the next five minutes feeling very nauseated and wanting to vomit. I then became unconscious.

That was my Great Morphine Experience. I guess that I don't have the genes to be an addict and write offbeat novels like the opiate-addicted author William S. Burroughs.

In other people, the protein that transports opiates operates so weakly that the morphine remains in the brain, causing massive respiratory depression, as well as nausea and vomiting. In another group of people the enzymes vary. For example, codeine works only because an enzyme in the body converts it to morphine. About 10% of people do not have this enzyme and, therefore, get no pain relief from codeine.

On-Demand Administration, where the patient self-administers the opiate dose via an intravenous delivery system until the pain is managed, has proven to be a big success. This is not surprising when you consider how huge the dosage range of these painkillers can be.

Other Drug Variability

In some cases, genetic variability means that drugs can kill a small percentage of people. This can happen with very powerful drugs that are used to treat very serious conditions.

Consider the drug 6-mercaptopurine, sometimes used to treat child leukaemia, severe rheumatoid arthritis and graft rejection. It is normally broken down by an enzyme in the body. But 1 in 300 people do not have this enzyme. In this case, the normally life-saving drug can kill.

At the moment, we do not have any simple way to find the one person in 300 who does not have the enzyme to break down 6-mercaptopurine. There are two tests for this. Both are quite different — one is a biochemical test, while the other is a DNA test. This is all still rather new. Even if patients take the DNA test, we are still not sure how to predict confidently what adjustments in dose need to be made.

Consider the drug abacavir, used to treat HIV/AIDS. In some

4–6% of people it causes a hypersensitivity reaction (HSR), and can sometimes kill. This HSR follows a well-described pathway — taking, on average, 11 days to become apparent, with 90% of patients presenting with symptoms in the first six weeks.

However, the test to identify the 4–6% of people who are hypersensitive to abacavir is much more satisfactory than the test for 6-mercaptopurine.

Consider the drug warfarin — an anti-clotting drug, often given to people to prevent the further formation of clots after a heart attack or a stroke. It is notoriously difficult to administer. Many medications, and even some foods, interfere with its activity. It also has a narrow therapeutic range. Too little will not prevent clots, but too much can cause bleeding and haemorrhage. The dosage needed to get the same results can vary by a factor of ten from patient to patient.

For several years we knew that two genes — Cytochrome P450 2C9 and the Vitamin K Epoxide Reductase Complex Subunit 1 — were involved in its activity. Finally, a study in 2008 found that if these genes were taken into account in working out the dose of warfarin, the patients fared much better. The patients who benefited the most were those at the extremes — those who took the smaller, or larger, doses of warfarin. These patients — those who took less than 21 mg or more than 49 mg of warfarin per week — made up 46% of the 4,300 patients in the study. However, the jury is still out on the usefulness of these DNA tests, because there is still no easy algorithm to allow the doctor to use the result of the tests to predict what change in warfarin dose is needed.

But then in February 2009, another gene involved in the metabolism of warfarin was discovered. Presumably, once this newly discovered gene is taken into account, the treatment of patients with warfarin will improve again.

Direct-to-Consumer DNA Tests

If you wish to spend the money ($1,000 or so), you can send a sample of your saliva to a company that will, in return, send you back a 'genomic profile'. While the test report may state that you have an increased risk of heart disease or diabetes, it may also tell you that 'the test is not a clinical service to be used as the basis for making clinical decisions'. Welcome to the new world of DTC DNA, or Direct-to-Consumer DNA tests.

There are a few things to realise about these 'genomic profiles'.

First, they do not look at all of your DNA, but at much less than 1% of it. Which bits are looked at will change the consumer's risk profile (please note, the person who is paying for this so-called medical service is known as a 'consumer', not a 'patient'). A good example of this is Type 2 Diabetes. Some 25% of Europeans will suffer from this disease during their lifetime. In 2007, there were fewer than ten DNA markers known for Type 2 Diabetes. Based on those markers, the consumers would have been sold a risk assessment. But since 2007 there have been two major updates in our knowledge of Type 2 Diabetes, with each update adding more DNA markers. After the first update, 'more than 11% of people went from being told that they were at above-average risk to below average or vice versa; after the second update more than 10% were similarly reclassified'. In other words, we still know too little about DNA to understand what these companies are selling.

Second, 'many of the diseases listed by the direct-to-consumer testing companies (e.g. diabetes, various cancers and heart disease) are so-called complex diseases thought to be caused by multiple gene variants, interactions among these variants, interactions between variants and environmental factors'. In other words, we still do not fully understand how these diseases work. But the DTC testing companies will ignore the thousands of possible interactions. They will sell you the information that you *probably* have one or two genes that could increase your risk of a specific illness.

Third, no test made by human beings is perfect, hence the use of the word 'probably' in the sentence above. For example, there is a genetic test for Bipolar Disease. But it's not a very good test. So, unfortunately, this test will wrongly report that more than 80% of those who actually do have Bipolar Disease do not have the supposed single gene for this disorder. And, on the other side, many people will be reported as having the gene when, in fact, they do not.

Fourth, we really still do not have the Big Picture of DNA. Human beings have about 20,000–23,000 genes. This is about the same number of genes as a pinot noir grape! So, obviously, we still have a very primitive understanding of exactly what a 'gene' is, and we clearly have a long way to go.

Fifth, these are still early days for DTC DNA testing. We have found only a minuscule fraction of the genes involved in various diseases. The vast majority of them are still to be found. Suppose that you pay the $1,000 for a genomic test, and the report states that you do not carry any genes associated with the likelihood of having a particular disease when you actually do carry the genes. Then you might decide that you can indulge in risky behaviour, your life becoming worse for having taken the test.

In early 2008, *The Observer* newspaper in the UK interviewed psychiatrist Professor Nick Craddock of

Cardiff University. He said, 'These tests will only worry, confuse and mislead the public and patients. There is a long way to go before we have genetic tests that may be helpful to patients. Using tests at the moment is only likely to cause harm.' In other words, our understanding of DNA is still very poor. There is absolutely no provision by the companies making money from DTC DNA testing to provide appropriate support and counselling for their patients (or 'consumers'). Professor David Collier, of the Institute of Psychiatry, London, said much the same thing: 'At best, these tests are clinically useless. At worst, their results could cause serious worries for patients.'

Future Horizons

Soon we will be able to map a person's entire DNA cheaply and, more importantly, be able to understand what we find. We will be able to use this knowledge to work out who can benefit from a particular drug. Ideally, one day we will be able to identify the 'responders' (those who benefit from a particular drug) with a cheap and quick genetic test — and, at the same time, identify those who would have undesirable side effects.

Think back to the 90% of drugs that are sidelined because they are toxic to a tiny percentage of the population. In the future, we hope to be able to use these drugs only on the 99.99% of people who can benefit from them, and steer these drugs away from the 0.01% of people to whom they are toxic.

But before this can happen, we have a lot to learn about genetics.

Sir William Ostler said it all way back in 1892: 'If it were not for the great variability among individuals, medicine might as well be a science and not an art.'

References

Aldhous, Peter, 'Genes that tell an ever-changing story', *New Scientist*, 1 August 2009, p 12.

Burke, Wylie, et al., 'Translational genomics: seeking a shared vision of benefit', *The American Journal of Bioethics*, March 2008, Vol 8, Issue 3, pp 54–56.

'Discriminating on genes', *Nature*, 5 July 2007, p 2.

Hunter, David J., et al., 'Letting the genome out of the bottle — will we get our wish?', *The New England Journal of Medicine*, 10 January 2008, Vol 358, No 2, pp 105–107.

International Warfarin Pharmacogenetics Consortium, 'Estimation of the warfarin dose with clinical and pharmacogenetic data', *The New England Journal of Medicine*, 19 February 2009, Vol 360, No 8, pp 753–764.

McKie, Robin, 'Internet gene tests provoke alarm', *The Observer*, 3 February 2008.

Reynolds, Kristen K., et al., 'Individualizing warfarin therapy', *Personalised Medicine*, February 2007, Vol 4, No 1, pp 11–31.

Roses, Allen D., 'Genome-based pharmacogenetics and the pharmaceutical industry', *Nature Reviews, Drug Discovery*, July 2002, pp 541–549.

Somogyi, Andrew A., et al., 'Pharmacogenetics of opioids', *Clinical Pharmacology & Therapeutics*, March 2007, Vol 81, No 3, pp 429–443.

mEAt ROts In Gut

(An IndIGEstIBLE TALE?)

Intellectually, I love vegetarianism. In fact, I was a vegetarian for many years. On the Big Scale, it's absolutely true that if you want to feed an entire population, vegetarian diets consume fewer resources than meat diets. And further, on the Small Scale, it's well known that a properly devised vegetarian diet can deliver real health benefits, including lower rates of obesity, heart disease and some cancers.

But I don't agree with claims that human beings were never meant to eat meat. Nor do I agree with those who reckon that meat will putrefy and rot in your gut, giving off toxins that cause many diseases, including insanity, premature ageing and (God Help Us) enfeeblement.

Meat Rots Before Elimination?

Here's the claim: 'It is a known fact that eating flesh of dead animals is hard to digest and some of it rots in the gut before elimination can take place and this putrefying residue is absorbed into the bloodstream and it poisons the entire system.' In human beings this 'poison' is supposed to cause '… premature ageing, fatigue, toxicity and worms feasting on this waste. The cells of the

Vegetarianism Good for the Planet?

In 1997, at the 24–26 July meeting of the Canadian Society of Animal Science in Montreal, David Pimentel, Professor of Ecology in Cornell University's College of Agriculture and Life Sciences, said: 'If all the grain currently fed to livestock in the United States were consumed directly by people, the number of people who could be fed would be nearly 800 million.'

However, sometimes livestock can graze on land that is too marginal to support agriculture. But most of the time this is not the case.

If you really want high efficiency in converting food to body mass, ignore cattle with their pathetic 10% conversion efficiency. Eat cockroaches, which convert 44% of their food to body mass. Or you might prefer chickens, which are pretty good at food-to-body mass conversion as well.

body must be supplied with the proper nourishment to efficiently eliminate this waste and when something blocks this process, the cells and organs deteriorate and die. By the time meat eaters reach the age of 50 years they will have accumulated a lot of undigested meat rotting in their gut.'

There is a particularly American version of this on the wonderful Urban Myths home page (snopes.com). It says: 'By the way, when they did an autopsy on John Wayne (Mr Macho himself) 40 pounds [18.14 kg] of impacted fecal matter was removed from his death-inducing cancerous colon. That's because Humans are not evolved for Animal eating.'

This is a complete fabrication, as Snopes points out furhter in their article. At the time of his death in 1979, the actor John Wayne was an American icon. He had already undergone several surgical operations for his cancer, which eventually killed him. It was obvious from his clinical course that the cancer killed him, so there was no medical or forensic reason for an autopsy. In fact, his family was so intent on keeping the fans and the media at bay that they had his body secretly transferred to a mortuary at 5.45 am for a quick funeral service, and then buried him immediately, without an identifying headstone. There was no autopsy and, hence, no '40 pounds of impacted fecal matter' to be found.

Evolved to Eat Meat

One variation of this Rotting Meat myth includes the assertion that the average American stores (presumably until they die) several kilograms of 'undigested, putrefying meat' in their intestines. The supposed reason for this is that human beings were not designed to eat meat.

But we have evolved to eat meat. Here's some proof.

First, the teeth in the human skull include both cutting incisors (as found in carnivores) and grinding molars (as found in herbivores). This combination makes us flexible omnivores. The incisors can generate an effective 'squash' of 2–3 kg, while the molars can generate about 90 kg.

In addition, the human gut has all the enzymes needed to digest meat.

Human beings have quite a long, and sophisticated, gut. Our stomachs probably evolved about 500 million years ago. Before then creatures had no jaws, so they would slowly digest all that they could swallow. However, with the development of the jaw, prehistoric fishes needed somewhere to store the stuff they had eaten and so developed a gut.

WE hAVE EVOLVED to EAT MEAT

The teeth in our skulls include both cutting incisors (as found in carnivores)
and grinding molars (as found in herbivores).
This combination makes us flexible omnivores.
The incisors can generate an effective 'squash' of 2–3 kilograms,
while the molars can generate about 90 kilograms.

UPPER TEETH

Central Incisor
Lateral Incisor
Canine
First Molar
Second Molar

Second Molar
First Molar
Canine
Lateral Incisor
Central Incisor

LOWER TEETH

SELECTIONS OF THE MEAT WE LOVE TO EAT

Enzyme and Surface

An enzyme is a chemical that makes a chemical reaction happen more quickly. Breaking down carbohydrates, fats and proteins into their constituent molecules happens through chemical reactions. So, of course, enzymes are involved.

Now here's a very fundamental truth of biochemistry. *Enzymes work only on a surface.*

Enzymes can act *only* on chemicals that they can get close to, i.e. chemicals on a surface of something. So if you just swallow your food without chewing it, the enzymes in your gut can break down the carbohydrates, fats and proteins on the surface of the ball of food. They cannot break down any carbohydrates, fats and proteins deep inside the ball of food – because they cannot get to them.

So part of the process of digestion is breaking down your food into smaller balls which, in total, have a bigger surface area. Chewing your food thoroughly can help digestion.

Digestion

The human gut is approximately 10 m long. The food enters at the mouth where you chew it, and where your saliva adds a few digestive enzymes. Then, after transit via the oesophagus, this food ends up in the stomach.

In the stomach, the enzyme called 'pepsin' attacks the proteins in meat. Pepsin has two main pathways of activity. First, it attacks collagen that makes up the main bulk of the connective tissue that joins the cells of the meat together. This allows the pepsin to get into the cells of the meat. Second, once it gets inside these cells, pepsin starts breaking down the long chains of amino acids into smaller chains.

Typically, some of the food will leave the stomach almost immediately. (We know that some carbohydrate foods leave the stomach almost immediately, because the blood glucose levels are already higher than fasting levels within 5–10 minutes of eating.) Overall, food will stay in the stomach for up to two and a half hours, before moving on to the next section, the small intestine. But the pepsin acting in the stomach digests only about 15% of the protein.

The small intestine does most of the digestion and absorption of what we eat. It takes about 2–6 hours to do so.

The pancreas is an organ that squirts various enzymes into the small intestine. These enzymes are very powerful, able to digest fats and carbohydrates, as well as proteins. With proteins, they break down the small chains of amino acids into even smaller chains. These enzymes are 'activated' only after they have been squirted out into the hollow tube of the small intestine — because they are so powerful that they can digest even the pancreas itself.

Bring on the Surface Area

The small intestine can absorb only via its internal surface. So it has lots of 'tricks' to increase its internal surface area.

First, it is not just a simple tube with a constant diameter. It has visible internal folds or pockets, called 'valvulae conniventes' (or the 'Folds of Kerckring'), which protrude as much as 8 mm into the internal 'lumen' (the hollow part of the tube). These folds increase the surface area by a factor of three.

Second, there are literally millions of small fingers, called villi, covering the surface of the small intestine. About 1 mm high, they increase the surface area by another factor of ten.

MEAt MY stOMACh

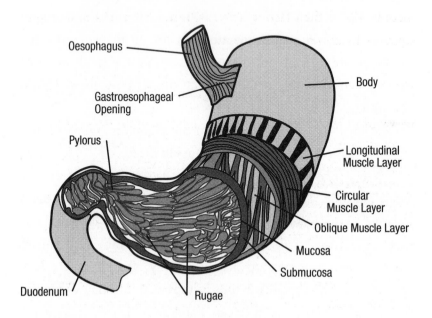

Oesophagus

Gastroesophageal
Opening

Pylorus

Body

Longitudinal
Muscle Layer

Circular
Muscle Layer

Oblique Muscle Layer

Mucosa

Submucosa

Duodenum

Rugae

THE STOMACH

In the stomach, the enzyme called 'pepsin' attacks the proteins
in meat. Pepsin has two main pathways of activity. First, it attacks
collagen that makes up the main bulk of the connective tissue
joining the cells of the meat together. This allows the pepsin
to get into the cells of the meat. Second, once it gets inside
the cells of which meat is made, pepsin starts breaking
down the long chains of amino acids into smaller chains.

Third, the villi in turn are covered by microvilli, as many as 1,000 to each cell lining the gut. These microscopic fingers are about 1 micrometre long (one-millionth of a metre) and 0.1 micrometres thick. They increase the internal surface area a further 20 times.

So the total internal surface area of the small intestine is increased by a factor of about 1,000, to about 250 m^2, roughly equal to the area of a tennis court.

Water and Digestion

Water is probably the only chemical for which practically everybody knows the formula – H_2O. (And perhaps the now infamous greenhouse gas, CO_2, is also in the process of becoming as well known.)

The reaction to make, and break, water can run in either direction, depending on where energy is applied.

$$2H_2O \leftrightarrows 2H_2 + O_2$$

This same reaction is essential for breaking down all three major foods – carbohydrates, fats and proteins.

Carbohydrates are made of repeating single sugars stuck together. The breakdown reaction involves taking an 'H' from one sugar, and an 'OH' from the next sugar, and so on. The 'H' and the 'OH' combine to make water, H_2O. So breaking down carbohydrates generates water.

Breaking down fats also makes water. (This is how camels survive – their hump is full of fat, not water.) A fat usually has three fatty acid molecules combined with a glycerol molecule. When they are split, three molecules of water are released.

Proteins are different – they need the addition of water to break them down. (Ever felt thirsty after a high-protein meal?) Proteins are strings of amino acids stuck together. To separate them, an 'H' is added to one amino acid, an 'OH' is added to the next, and so on.

The small intestine has a big job. Each day, it has to digest some 7–8 litres of liquid.

This liquid consists of about 1,000 ml of saliva from the mouth, 1,500 ml from the stomach, 1,000 ml from the pancreas, 1,000 ml of bile from the gall bladder, 1,800 ml from the small intestine itself and 200 ml from Bruner's Gland (located in the first few centimetres of the duodenum). Each day, your small intestine will absorb 'several hundred grams of carbohydrates, about 100 g of fat, 50–100 g of amino acids, 50–100 g of ions and 7–8 litres of water'.

Running at maximum capacity, each day it can absorb several kilograms of carbohydrates, 500 g of fat, about 600 g of protein and over 20 litres of water!

Break Down

The cells lining the gut have microscopic fingers on them called microvilli.

Enzymes are anchored or embedded in the actual walls of the microvilli. These enzymes start inside the body of the microvilli, and protrude through the wall of the microvilli into the hollow tube of the gut.

When you eat food, these enzymes break down the chains of amino acids (in the meat) into tiny chains of three and two amino acids and, sometimes, even single amino acids. These are carried into the cells lining the gut and broken down (if necessary) into single amino acids. Then they are passed right through the cell out to the other side, and then into a vein that carries the individual amino acids to the Big Organ, the liver, for further processing.

The gut contents are then moved from the small intestine into the large intestine where water and some electrolytes are removed. The time taken for this transit is much greater, ranging from 14 to 80 hours.

The various transit times are affected by many factors, including genetics, quantity of fibre in the diet, size of meals, age, gender, smoking, exercise, and so on.

So yes, our human gut actually has all the mechanisms needed for digesting the proteins of meat.

Hunger Pangs

True hunger pangs begin only 12 to 24 hours after eating. They reach their maximum strength three to four days later and then weaken.

Meat and Fullness

Every now and then, after a week or so of not eating meat, I have what I call a 'meat hunger'. I want some meat and, after eating it, I then feel full.

A few years ago, on an American holiday, we happened across a bakery having a lunchtime barbecue. My son and I ate enormous amounts of meat, including beef, chicken, bacon, pork, ham and turkey – it was not a vegetarian bakery. (Anyhow, the whole point of travel is to experience what the locals experience.) That night, I had absolutely no hunger. The next morning we were still not hungry. Slight twinges of hunger began to appear around lunchtime – a whole day after the gigantic meat meal.

Yes, meat can give a sense of 'fullness' or 'satisfaction' that carbohydrates do not. We are not sure why. But this 'fullness' does not mean that the meat is not being digested, and that it is rotting in your gut.

Toothpaste

However, in each part of the gut, the mushy contents tend to move through as a unit, similar to toothpaste being squeezed out of its container. These are thoroughly mixed in together before they eventually escape to the outside world.

Those parts of the mush that were originally meat are not separated out, and are not specially kept aside to rot quietly. If you want your meat to rot, you need to put it to the side of your plate ...

References

Bodanis, David, *The Body Book: A Fantastic Voyage to the World Within*, Little, Brown & Co., 1984, pp 210–212.

Graff, J., et al., 'Gastrointestinal mean transit times in young and middle-aged healthy subjects', *Clinical Physiology*, March 2001, Vol 21, No 2, pp 253–259.

Guyton, Arthur C. and Hall, John E., *A Textbook of Medical Physiology*, 9th edition, Pennsylvania: W.B. Saunders Company, 1996, pp 793–844.

Mikkelson, Barbara and David P., 'Meat your maker', 31 December 2005, http://www.snopes.com/horrors/gruesome/fecalcolon.asp.

Shroud of Turin

In 1898, the city of Turin in northern Italy was celebrating the 400th anniversary of the inauguration of its major church, the Cathedral of St John the Baptist. As part of the celebrations, Secondo Pia, working in the relatively new field of photography, was commissioned to photograph a famous local relic stored in one of the chapels of the cathedral. The relic was a linen shroud or 'winding sheet', supposedly used to wrap the dead body of Jesus Christ. On 28 May, as Secondo Pia processed the glass plate to get the negative image (from which a positive photograph would later be made), he was astonished to see a positive human-like image on the glass.

To him, at that moment, the only possible interpretation was that he was looking at the face of Christ. And that's where and when all the current hype about the now famous Shroud of Turin began.

Biblical History of Shroud

According to the New Testament of the Christian Bible, Jesus Christ lived, performed miracles, was crucified and died. After his death, a man known only as Joseph of Arimathea became involved with the disposal of Christ's Body. According to the authoritative *Catholic Encyclopaedia* of 1910, Joseph of Arimathea 'was a wealthy Israelite' (*Matthew* 27: 57), 'a good and a just man' (*Luke* 23: 50), 'who was also himself looking for the kingdom of God' (*Mark* 15: 43). He is also called by St Mark and by St Luke a *bouleutes* — literally, a 'senator', i.e. a member of the Sanhedrin or Supreme Council of the Jews.

Joseph was a disciple of Jesus, probably since he first heard Christ preaching in Judea (*John* 2: 23), but he did not declare himself as such 'for fear of the Jews' (*John* 19: 38). On account of this secret allegiance to Jesus, he did not consent to His condemnation by the Sanhedrin (*Luke* 23: 51), and was most likely absent from the meeting which sentenced Jesus to death (cf. *Mark* 14: 64).

At this turbulent time, so soon after Christ's death, it was a risky affair to be linked to Jesus Christ. Even so, Joseph bravely petitioned Pontius Pilate for the Body, and was successful. He and Nicodemus (who came with many kilograms of spices used for anointing a body) wrapped the Body in fine linen and laid it out in a brand-new unused tomb. They closed the tomb by rolling a great stone up against the opening.

Three days later, Mary Magdalene went to the tomb and was astonished to find that the great stone had been rolled away. Then, according to *John*, 20: 2–7, 'She ran therefore and cometh to Simon Peter and to the other disciple whom Jesus loved and saith to them: They have taken away the Lord out of the sepulchre: and we know not where they have laid him. Peter therefore went out, and the other disciple: and they came to the sepulchre. And they both ran together: and that other disciple did outrun Peter and came first to the sepulchre. And when he stooped down, he saw the linen cloths lying: but yet he went not in. Then cometh Simon Peter, following him, and went into the sepulchre: and saw the linen cloths lying. And the napkin that had been about his head, not lying with the linen cloths, but apart, wrapped up into one place.'

This is the original story of the Shroud, or the Holy Winding Sheet of Christ.

The Shroud Today

After that tumultuous day when St Peter first found the Holy Winding Sheet, for some unknown reason, it simply dropped out of sight. And it took well over a millennium before the Sheet — now known as the Shroud of Turin — made an appearance.

Today, the Sheet called the Shroud of Turin is a long, skinny rectangular piece of cloth, about 4.34 m long by 1.09 m wide.

If you look carefully, you can just see two faded yellow–brown images. They show the entire front and back of a naked man with his hands covering his groin. The man is thin, heavily bearded and about 1.8 m in height — tall for a person of that time in the Middle East. There are stains from nail wounds in the feet, shoulder abrasions, and stains from puncture wounds on the head. There are also flogging injuries on the man's back, and a wound through his left wrist. The images are consistent with a man being laid on a long cloth with his feet at one end and his head in the middle, and then the other half of the cloth being folded back over him.

The images are very faded, and difficult to see.

Before examining its authenticity here's a little on the history of the Shroud.

Holy Winding Sheet, 1353+

In the year 1353, on 20 June, the famed knight Geoffroy de Charny, the Seigneur or Lord of Lirey, founded a church in Lirey. A smaller chapel inside this church was set aside to show, for veneration, the Holy Winding Sheet (as it was known back then).

Shrouded in controversy

After Christ's death, it was still a risky affair to be linked to Jesus Christ. Even so, Joseph bravely petitioned Pilate for the Body, and was successful. He and Nicodemus (who came with many kilograms of spices for anointing a body) wrapped the Body in fine linen, and laid it out in a brand-new unused tomb. They closed the tomb by rolling a great stone up against the opening.

THE IMAGE ON THE SHROUD SHOWS A THIN AND HEAVILY BEARDED MAN

The images on the shroud are very faded, and difficult to see.

This is the very first well-documented report of the existence of the Holy Winding Sheet after the Resurrection of Christ.

In those days, there was a good living to be made from charging the faithful to view biblical relics. Within a few years, by 1357, the Shroud had become a nice little earner, many pilgrims coming from far and wide to see the one-and-only, the true and the original Burial Shroud of Christ. According to *National Geographic*, 'the 14th century, especially, was notorious for relic mongering, when chicanery and fraud abounded'.

But Bishop Henri de Poitiers of Troyes was sceptical about the Shroud, and carried out an investigation into its validity. This ancient town of Troyes (situated about 16 km to the north of Lirey) has a very long history, getting its first bishop in the early 300s. With regard to the wars of the times, politically Troyes is very strategically located, being about 130 km to the east of Paris, and about 100 km south of Reims, the capital of Champagne. The small village of Lirey (where the Winding Sheet was held) was part of the diocese, or administration, of Troyes. The bishop found that the Sheet was a fake, a mere painting, and so it was quietly taken off the Biblical Relics Circuit.

Holy Winding Sheet, 1389+

In 1389, about three decades later, after all the fuss had died down, the Holy Winding Sheet went on its First Comeback Tour on the Biblical Relics Circuit, again lightening the purses of the faithful.

This time Bishop Pierre d'Arcis, the new bishop of Troyes, denounced it as a fraud. He wrote to Pope Clement VII (a member of the 'breakaway' Avignon Papacy in France, who reigned from 1378 to 1394), saying that with regard to the Holy Winding Sheet, the canons of the church at Lirey had 'falsely and deceitfully … with avarice … procured for their church a certain cloth on which was cunningly painted … the image of one man … pretending that this was the actual Shroud in which our Saviour Jesus Christ was enfolded in the tomb.'

Bishop d'Arcis thought it scandalous that 'it was then being exhibited by the Canons of Lirey in such a way that the populace believed that it was the authentic shroud of Jesus Christ'. He then referred back to the research of his predecessor, Bishop Henri de Poitiers, who personally knew that this Holy Winding Sheet was a fraud, because 'after diligent inquiry and examination' he had found that the Shroud 'was cunningly painted, the truth being attested by the artist who had painted it'. In other words, Bishop de Poitiers had tracked down the very artist who had manufactured this relic. This letter, in which Bishop d'Arcis states that the artist confessed to manufacturing this forgery of the Winding Sheet of Christ, still exists today.

In response, Pope Clement VII declared in a Papal Bull that the Sheet could be exhibited as an object of pilgrimage and devotion, but only if it was made perfectly clear that this sheet was just a 'representation' of the original shroud used to wrap Christ. 'The pope, without absolutely prohibiting the exhibition of the Shroud, decided … that in the future when it was shown to the people, the priest should declare in a loud voice that it was not the real shroud of Christ, but only a picture made to represent it.'

Holy Winding Sheet, 1418+

But some people thought there was still some life left in the Shroud as a Holy Relic.

By 1418, the Hundred Years War (which ran from 1337 to 1453) was raging. To protect the Holy Winding Sheet, the canons of the church in Lirey entrusted it to Humbert, the then Lord of Lirey.

After his death, and as the war was winding down, the canons of Lirey asked for it to be returned. However, Humbert's widow Margaret (the granddaughter of Geoffroy de Charny) refused to return it to the canons, despite their many requests. Instead, she generously gave this very same Winding Sheet to Louis, Duke of Savoy, in 1452. He too was generous and, in exchange, gave her two castles.

The Sheet has remained with the House of Savoy from then up to the present day. (The House of Savoy grew so much that it later became the ruler of Italy — the Italian Monarchy — until 1946.)

We know that the Sheet was at Chambéry (the capital of Savoy in France) in 1453. Chambéry is about 330 km to the south-southwest of Lirey, and much closer to the Italian border. In 1464, the Duke of Savoy agreed to make an annual payment to the canons of Lirey, if they would drop all claims to ownership of the Winding Sheet.

In 1467, the then Duke of Savoy, Amadeus IX, built a Ducal Chapel (the Sainte Chapelle) in Chambéry especially to house the Holy Winding Sheet.

Holy Winding Sheet, 1471+

The passage of a century of time, as well as a different political climate, had reversed opinions as to the authenticity of the Holy Winding Sheet.

Pope Sixtus IV (who was pope from 1471 to 1484) wrote that in this Shroud, 'men may look upon the true blood and portrait of Jesus Christ himself'. (As an aside, Sixtus IV looked after his own family very well indeed, was a patron of the arts and letters — e.g. he built the Sistine Chapel — and vastly improved the sanitation of Rome.)

Pope Julius II (who was pope from 1503 to 1513) agreed. He mentioned in his Papal Bull *Romanus Pontifex* of 25 April 1506, the 'most famous Shroud in which our Savior was wrapped when he lay in the tomb and which is now honorably and devoutly preserved in a silver casket'. (As an aside, Julius II was a very successful warrior pope who re-established the Pontifical States and helped free Italy from France. As one of the greatest papal patrons of the arts he commissioned Michelangelo to paint the ceiling of the Sistine Chapel. He also had three daughters.)

While stored in Chambéry in a casket, the Winding Sheet was almost consumed in a fire in the chapel in 1532. Some of the silver on the inside of the casket melted, and fell onto corners of the folded Winding Sheet, permanently marking it. The Shroud also suffered some charring and water damage, which is still visible today.

Shroud of Turin, 1694

In 1578, the Duke of Savoy left Chambéry for his new capital of Turin in northern Italy, some 150 km to the west-southwest. The Winding Sheet went along with him. It finally wound up in a specially built shrine in the Royal Chapel of the Cathedral of St John the Baptist in Turin in 1694 — hence the name the 'Shroud of Turin'. The architect of the chapel was the mathematician Guarino Guarini. It has been in the Guarini Chapel ever since, apart from a brief period during World War II.

In 1958, Pope Pius XII approved of the image from the Shroud being used in association with the devotion to the Holy Face of Jesus. This was celebrated every Shrove Tuesday. (Shrove Tuesday is the last day of 'regular' life before the start of Lent — a period of fasting and prayer which begins on the next day, Ash Wednesday.)

On 12 April 1997, the Shroud was again almost consumed in a fire which broke out in the Guarini Chapel of the cathedral in Turin. Mr Mario Trematore was just one fireman out of 140 who came from as far away as Milan, 120 km away, to fight the blaze. He used a hammer to smash through the bulletproof glass, grabbed the silver box holding the Shroud with both hands, and ran with it to safety.

Image from Body to Shroud

If the Shroud were a simple forgery manufactured in the Middle Ages, it's easy to understand how the image arrived on the linen.

But what if it were really the actual Shroud used to wrap the Body of Christ? How did the image transfer from the Body to the Shroud?

There are many theories.

Theory Number One. The Body was anointed with oils and spices. The habit of anointing the corpse was common in the Middle East at that time. These oils 'somehow' transferred to the Body, creating an image. But why has this never happened with all the other corpses that have been anointed and then wrapped in a winding cloth?

And if the image did come from direct contact with the Body of Christ, it would have been distorted, thanks to having been wrapped around the Body. Dead bodies were indeed wrapped at that time in the Middle East. However, they were never simply laid on a long cloth, with the other half of the cloth then folded over the body.

Theory Number Two. Vapours from the Body made the image. This theory (called 'Vaporography'), first put forth by Dr Paul Vignon before the French Academy of Sciences in 1902, says that the corpse had sweat on it and that the urea in the sweat fermented, creating ammonia. This ammonia then wafted gently from the Body onto the linen. There were already various oils and spices on the linen. The ammonia reacted with the impregnated cloth to produce an image.

One problem is that the image is sharp and defined, but vapours are notorious for going anywhere and everywhere. And why has an image of a body never been transferred, in all the other cases of sweaty bodies that have been anointed and then wrapped in a winding cloth?

Theory Number Three. Lynn Picknett and Clive Prince claim that the image on the Shroud is a photograph. Leonardo da Vinci, they claim, had been commissioned to make this Shroud by Pope Innocent VIII. So Leonardo — they claim, with no proof at all — invented photography a few centuries before everybody else. They further claim that Leonardo did some advanced photo-editing, and photographically joined his own head with the body of an unknown person whom he had crucified — just to make this image.

Theory Number Four. It is claimed that Christ was resurrected by the total conversion of His corporeal Body into energy, on the third day after he died. This energy then somehow 'burned' His image into the linen winding cloth.

One problem with this theory is the sheer magnitude of the energy released. Two kilograms of matter will, if totally converted into energy, deliver about 47 megatons of energy. That is roughly the amount of energy delivered by the biggest hydrogen bomb ever exploded — called the Tsar Bomba, it was detonated by the Soviets on 30 October 1961. The fireball from this blast was enormous — 8 km in diameter. If the Body of Christ (weighing approximately 60–80 kg) had been turned into energy, the yield would have been about 30 to 40 times greater. Surely someone in nearby Jerusalem would have noticed?

There are many other theories, none of them scientifically

valid. The only way out is to conclude that either the image on the Shroud is indeed a miracle (i.e. not subject to the laws of nature) or just the work of a forger.

Authenticity — Many Shrouds

The first problem with the Shroud of Turin being the True and Original burial shroud of Jesus Christ is simple.

There are another 40 or more burial shrouds of Jesus Christ, each claiming to be the only True and Original Shroud. They include the shrouds at Besançon, Cadouin and Champagne in France, and Xabregas in Portugal.

The only thing special about the Shroud of Turin is that, thanks to accidents of history, it's the most famous.

Authenticity — No Comment

The writers of the Gospel considered the Resurrection of Christ to be a miracle.

Surely the Gospel writers would have also thought the transference of the image of Christ to his Winding Sheet to be a miracle?

So why did they not mention it?

Authenticity — Sudden Fading

The Shroud first came to notice in the 14th century. We know that 'the witnesses of the fifteenth and early sixteenth centuries speak of the image as being then so vivid that the blood seemed freshly shed'.

But today the image on the Shroud is so faded as to be almost invisible.

How could the image keep its brightness for 13 centuries, and then lose it in the next five centuries? On the other hand, this is exactly what we would expect to find if it were a 14th century forgery.

Authenticity — Blood

There are reddish stains on the image's wrists, feet and left side of the chest. Iron, proteins and porphyrins are found in blood. They are also found in these stains. Surely this must mean that the stains are the blood of Christ?

Nope.

First, only fresh blood is red. After a short time, it darkens to deep brown or black.

Second, iron, proteins and porphyrins are indeed found in blood — but they are also found in many red paints and pigments. Walter McCrone, a member of the American Academy of Forensic Sciences, has testified in court on forensic cases. He analysed the 'blood' on the Shroud, and found that it was red ochre and vermilion in a collagen tempera medium.

Third, the element sodium is very abundant in blood. But there's no sodium in the stains on the Shroud.

Fourth, if it were proven to be blood (and it never has been, and it's the wrong colour anyway) a medieval artist could have used the blood of any animal.

Authenticity — Weave Pattern of Linen

The linen is a herringbone-twill weave.

This type of weave was not known in the Middle East at the time of Christ. However, it was common in medieval Europe.

Authenticity — No Brush Strokes

It is true to say that there are no signs of brush strokes on the Shroud.

Does this prove that it cannot have been painted?

Nope.

First, a technique called 'rubbing' has been used to give a result remarkably similar to the image on the Shroud. The technique called 'Brass Rubbing' involves laying a sheet of paper on top of a brass image (usually a face or a full human figure), and then carefully rubbing the paper with graphite, chalk or soft wax. And yes, 'rubbing' automatically gives a 'negative' image.

Second, there are ways to apply paint without leaving brush strokes. In 1994, Drs Craig and Bresee wrote in the *Journal of Imaging Science and Technology* of their experiments with the Carbon Dust Drawing Technique. This technique was known in medieval times, and has long been used by medical illustrators. It involves gently brushing a dry powder (charcoal or ground carbon) onto a surface with a soft artist's paintbrush, with many short delicate strokes, each from a different angle. Each brush stroke makes hardly any difference, but many strokes do. They were able to reproduce many of the features of the image on the Shroud of Turin, including a complete lack of brush strokes.

Authenticity — 3-D Information

In 1977, Donald Lynne and Jean Lorre announced that the image on the Shroud had a supposedly unique mathematical property. If you assume that the darkest parts of the image are the ones closest to the Body, and the lightest parts the ones furthest away, then you can reconstruct a 3-D image of the face. This was absolutely amazing — if it was unique to the Shroud of Turin.

But it was not. In fact, it was incredibly easy to duplicate. Doctors Craig and Bresee used the Carbon Dust Drawing Technique to make their own image on a shroud. And yes, it had the same 3-D information.

Authenticity — Pollen from Jerusalem

It was claimed by Max Frei that pollen similar to the pollen found around Jerusalem was detected on the Shroud.

First, there are doubts as to the credibility of Max Frei as a scientist. He was the man who claimed that the so-called Hitler Diaries of 1983 were genuine. They were later found to be fake, after he had authenticated them.

Second, trade between Palestine and Europe existed in medieval times and, therefore cloth (carrying pollen) could easily have been brought from Jerusalem.

Authenticity — Carbon Dating

In 1988, the Vatican sent three postage-sized samples of cloth from the Shroud of Turin to three independent laboratories in England, Switzerland and the USA. They used radiocarbon dating to measure the harvesting date of the flax, from which the cloth of the Shroud was woven. They arrived at dates somewhere between 1260 and 1390 AD (with 95% certainty).

As a result, the Roman Catholic Church announced that the Shroud of Turin was not the original shroud used to wrap Christ — but it also announced that Christians could venerate the Shroud as a memorial to Christ, or as an old (i.e. from the 1300s) imagined pictorial image of how Christ could have looked, if he was European.

Some people have argued that this dating is wrong.

First, they claim that the samples did not come from the original Shroud but from additions that were invisibly woven into the cloth to repair the damage of the 1532 fire. There are a few problems with this argument. If the additions were invisibly woven in, how can they tell that they were present? If the additions were not invisibly melded in, then surely the Vatican would have sent an original part of the Shroud, not something dating to 1532.

Second, they claim that extra new carbon (rich in Carbon-14) has been added. This could come from the hands of the pilgrims touching it in its early days, or from bacteria that have invaded the fabric of the Shroud. Yes, carbon that was rich in Carbon-14 would indeed alter the measured date to appear more recent. But, the amount of carbon needed to shift the date from 33 AD to 1300 AD would be equal to twice the weight of the entire Shroud. Surely, somebody would have noticed that the Shroud had tripled in weight and thickness.

The More Things Change …

On one hand, there is a cloth that suddenly appears out of the blue about 13 centuries after the event. In one of the earliest reports about this cloth a bishop discussed the confession of the person who forged the image. The chemicals that make up the image are clearly identified as paint. And radiocarbon dating places the fabric to around the time of the forger.

On the other hand, there is a cloth bearing an image for which there is no plausible explanation (other than being made by a forger).

It took about six centuries and lots of science to reach the same conclusion as Pope Clement VII did in the 14th century. Except for the fact that the Shroud is made from linen, it seems that people are having the wool pulled over their eyes.

References

Cadena, Richard, 'Joe Nickell, skeptical investigator', *The Skeptic* (Australian edition), Summer 2001, Vol 21, No 4, pp 52–57.

Craig, Emily A. and Bresee, Randall R., 'Image formation and the Shroud of Turin', *Journal of Imaging Science and Technology*, 1994, Vol 34, No 1.

Edwards, Harry, 'Travels of a skeptic', *The Skeptic* (Australian edition), Summer 1998, Vol 18, No 4, p 52.

Gigot, F., 'Joseph of Arimathea', *The Catholic Encyclopedia*, New York: Robert Appleton Company, 1910, Vol 8. Retrieved 7 August 2009 from New Advent: http://www.newadvent.org/cathen/08520a.htm.

Kelly, Lynne, *The Skeptic's Guide to the Paranormal*, Crows Nest, NSW: Allen & Unwin, 2004, pp 20–33.

Picknett, Lynn and Prince, Clive, *Turin Shroud: In Whose Image?*, New York: HarperCollins, 1994.

Thurston, H., 'The Holy Shroud (of Turin)', *The Catholic Encyclopedia*. New York: Robert Appleton Company, 1912, Vol 13. Retrieved 7 August 2009 from New Advent: http://www.newadvent.org/cathen/13762a.htm.

Vikan, Gary, 'Debunking the Shroud: made by human hands', *Biblical Archaeology Review*, November/December 1998, Vol 24, No 26.

Weaver, Kenneth F., 'Science seeks to solve the mystery of the Shroud', *National Geographic*, June 1980, pp 730–752.

mOBILE PhONES ANd PEtroL StAtIons

(FuELLING thE RuMOurs)

Mobile phones provide us with a really good example of just how irrational we human beings can be.

These phones are blamed for all kinds of health problems, ranging from brain cancer to memory loss. There's not a lot of real evidence for this — and it certainly doesn't stop people from using their phones.

However, mobile phones are the cause of a lot of stupidity in the hands of pedestrians and motorists. It is well established that talking on a phone while driving makes you as incompetent a driver as if you were drunk. And that's just talking on the phone, using a hands-free set. The mere act of concentrating on the phone call makes you a less capable driver. Holding the phone makes you even less capable. In fact, in some states around the world it's illegal to use a hand-held phone when driving a car. But people will still do it.

Not surprisingly, given the little pictures displayed on petrol pumps, many people believe that mobile phones are dangerous to use while refuelling their car's petrol tank. Yet there's pretty much no evidence that using a mobile phone at a petrol station will set off a conflagration.

How much evidence? How about not even one case in the history of the human race, and that's taking into account every single petrol station that has ever been built, in every country of every continent!

And yet people still believe this myth.

The Email

Every month or so, I get an earnest email warning me of the hazards of using my mobile phone on the forecourt of a petrol station. Almost every time, the email mentions the Shell Oil Company as its source, or has the Shell Oil Company in the 'sig' (signature) lines at the bottom of the email.

And almost every time, it quotes the same three incidents of petrol fires that occur while a mobile phone owner is refuelling the car.

The first incident has the mobile phone sitting innocently on the boot of the car, not far from the open petrol tank. The phone rings, generating an instant ball of fire.

The second episode has a person speaking on the phone while refuelling. Again, a conflagration ensues, leading to the person suffering very nasty facial burns.

In the third occurrence, the owner is refuelling when the phone in a pocket suddenly rings. Even before they answer the phone a fire somehow erupts, in this case causing unfortunate burns to the person's groin and thigh.

This email (about mobile phones causing petrol station fires) has been traced back to a hoax email that originated in Southeast Asia around 1999. In June 2002, it landed in the inbox of a Shell employee in Jamaica. He rebroadcast it, but with the Shell Company signature now added to the email. This accidental, non-approved signature gave the hoax more credibility.

MOBILEs + petroL = the BIG BANG theory

Mobile phones are blamed for all kinds of health problems, ranging from brain cancer to memory loss. There's not a lot of real evidence for this – and it certainly doesn't stop people from using their phones.

With many a warning sign at petrol pumps, there is a general belief that mobile phones are dangerous to use while you are refuelling your car's petrol tank.
However, there's pretty much no evidence that using a mobile phone in a petrol station will set off a conflagration.*

*Conflagration is an uncontrolled burning that threatens human life.

Tiny Seed of Truth

Like all good myths, this one has a tiny seed of truth in it.

Mobile phones get their power from their internal battery. Battery technology has always lagged behind electronics technology. Early mobile phone batteries had a few problems. They were heavy. They didn't store a lot of energy. They would not recharge fully, unless they were flattened fully (the so-called memory effect). And after a relatively small number of cycles of 'charge-and-discharge', they would die.

In the 1990s, these batteries were NiCad (Nickel Cadmium) batteries. They were replaced by NiMH (Nickel Metal Hydride) batteries which, in turn, were replaced by Li (Lithium) batteries. As the phone battery evolved, it became more complicated. In fact, the lithium phone battery is a Smart Battery — it has its own internal electronics to stop it from being flattened so much that it suffers permanent damage, and to keep the charging time as short as possible, etc.

Thermal Runaway

One advantage of lithium batteries is that they are lighter. But many lithium batteries use cobalt oxide, which can undergo 'Thermal Runaway'. According to the computer magazine *PC World*, '. . . when you heat this material up, it can reach an onset temperature that begins to self-heat and progresses into fire and explosion'.

Various experts recommend that you do not leave your laptop or mobile phone in the car on a hot day. A temperature of 60°C is enough to initiate Thermal Runaway.

Modern lithium batteries can store quite a lot of energy. They can keep a phone running for several days, slowly giving out this energy in tiny amounts.

But if all this energy were to be released in a fraction of a second, a lot of heat could be generated.

And yes, there have been cases of lithium batteries in laptop computers spontaneously overheating, warping the laptop's case, scorching the wooden desk on which it had been left and even bursting into flame. As a result, the manufacturer concerned, Sony, had to recall and replace 9.6 million laptop computer batteries in 2006. At the time, this was the world's biggest recall of consumer electronics. The computer companies involved were Dell, Apple, Toshiba and Lenovo.

But this recall was dwarfed in 2007. According to *The Washington Post*, 'Nokia offered to replace as many as 46 million cellphone batteries made by Matsushita Electrical Industrial as some may overheat, in what would be the largest voluntary consumer electronics recall. Nokia ... said there were about 100 cases of overheating, with no reports of serious injury or damage to property. The affected Nokia-brand BL-5C batteries were made by Matsushita from December 2005 to November 2006.'

Cell or Mobile?

In Australia, we call them 'mobile phones' because they are mobile and we can carry them around with us.

In the USA, they call them 'cellular phones' or 'cell phones', because mobile phone technology is based on dividing the landscape into little 'cells'. Inside each 'cell', all the cell phones each talk to the same phone tower. If the phone moves to another cell, then there is a 'handover' at the boundary, and the next phone tower takes over the job of talking to the phone.

Nokia said that 'the BL-5C batteries ... could potentially experience overheating initiated by a short circuit while charging'. Matsushita said that there had been 'a rare problem in the process of manufacturing battery cells ... rather than in the design of the batteries'.

Petrol Station Fire?

So, has a mobile phone ever set off a petrol station fire?

No, according to the Australian Transport Safety Bureau. They looked at 243 petrol station fires worldwide, happening in the 11 years between 1993 and 2004. They did not find a single case.

And no, according to the Australian Mobile Telecommunications Association, who in 2003 said, 'There is no evidence whatsoever that a mobile phone has ever caused an explosion at a petrol station.'

No, according to the American Petroleum Institute, which notes, 'We can find no evidence of someone using a cell phone causing any kind of accident, no matter how small, at a gas station anywhere in the world.'

And no again, according to Robert Renkes, a spokesman for the American Petroleum Institute, who said, 'We have not found a cell phone responsible for any fire since the beginning of mankind.'

And finally no, according to the popular *Mythbusters* TV show, which tried mightily with their considerable skills to make a mobile phone explode a chamber full of petrol vapour, and failed. (Mind you, petrol vapour will explode only when it makes up between 2–8% of the air volume. See also 'Exploding Car' chapter, p 187ff.)

To summarise, there has never been a single verified case of a mobile phone, under its normal operating conditions, setting off a petrol station fire.

So Why the Myth?

It is 'theoretically' possible to set off a petrol fire with a mobile phone. However, two very special conditions are needed.

First, the phone has to make a spark. Second, the spark has to ignite the petrol vapour. But remember, the petrol vapour has to be in the range of 2–8% by volume — if it's higher or lower, you can make all the sparks you want, but the petrol vapour will not ignite.

So yes, there is easily enough energy in the battery to make a spark. The amount of energy needed for a spark to ignite petrol vapour is 0.2 millijoules. This is roughly 50 million times smaller than the energy stored in a fully charged phone battery (about 10 kJ).

The problem here for our email myth is that the phone is not designed to make sparks. In fact, part of its design brief is to not make sparks.

There are a few unlikely scenarios that could possibly lead to a spark.

The lithium battery could explode while charging, if its internal regulator circuit was very faulty, and in a very specific way. But you don't normally simultaneously charge and use your mobile phone while refuelling your car. And having the internal battery regulator circuit fail at the same time is very unlikely.

Second, it's possible, but very unlikely, that the internal electronics of the phone (not the battery) could fail and make a spark. But this spark from the internal electronics would be much too small to ignite a petrol–air vapour, because all the internal electronics of the phone run at a very low power rating. Another problem in this unlikely scenario is that it would take much longer than a typical refuelling time for the petrol vapour to build up inside the phone to the critical concentration level (of around 2–8% petrol vapour).

Another unlikely scenario is that the battery could fall out of your phone, while it's jiggling around in your pocket. So assume you would have a loose and fully charged battery in your pocket. But it would be almost impossible for random metal objects in your pocket (e.g. keys, coins, paperclips) to touch the electrical contacts on the battery. This is because the electrical contacts have been designed to stop sparking. They are located slightly lower than the surface of the battery and/or are separated from each other by raised plastic strips.

Anyhow, why worry about the tiny 50 g phone battery when you have bigger batteries in such items as your iPod, CD player and mini-torch? In fact, if you are worried about taking a battery into a petrol station, don't forget the big 15 kg car battery that powers all the electrics in your car.

Electric Fields?

Okay, so it's very unlikely for a mobile phone to generate a spark from either its internal electronics or from its battery.

But don't mobile phones emit an electric field? And don't electric fields cause the luminous sparks called 'St Elmo's Fire'? So can't the electric field of a mobile phone cause sparks?

Okay, mobile phones do emit electric fields. And yes, St Elmo's Fire is a strange blue or violet glow, often accompanied by a distinct buzzing or hissing sound, and is a high-temperature plasma. It has been seen by sailors at sea in thunderstorms for thousands of years. But St Elmo's Fire needs an enormous electric field to generate it — somewhere around 100,000–3,000,000 volts/metre. This is much greater than the pathetic electric field of 2–5 volts/metre generated by a mobile phone with its tiny 3.6 volt battery.

Yes, there are cases where this tiny electric field of 2–5 volts/metre has interfered with heart monitors and infant incubators in hospitals, and with electronic equipment in aeroplanes. However, the electric field from a mobile phone has never been known to set off a fire in a petrol station. There is not one single case on record.

And consider that, in the UK, about 200 Shell petrol stations have mobile phone towers in the tall petrol price indicators, which stand right there on the forecourt, a few metres from the petrol pumps. The towers put out a lot more grunt than your small

Mobile Phone Tower Hysteria

Mobile phone towers are a cause of much worry – but for no good reason.

The maximum theoretical power that a GSM (Global System for Mobile communications) mobile phone can generate is 2 watts. But because of the way that the phone output is switched on and off, the power is never more than 0.25 watts. And this would be the case only when you are at the maximum possible distance from the mobile phone base station. When you are close to it, the power that your phone generates is a lot less.

But a mobile phone tower generates a lot more power – up to 1,500 watts per frequency channel. So let's compare a mobile phone tower 50 m away to a mobile phone held only a few centimetres from your head. Measured at your head, the electric and magnetic fields are about 50–100 times smaller from the phone tower than from your phone.

So why do people demonstrate against mobile phone towers? Why don't they demonstrate against the electric fields from the Sun?

After all, the electric field from the Sun is about four times greater than that from a mobile phone, or 200–400 times greater than that from a mobile phone tower.

mobile phone. The mobile phone towers have never been implicated in any petrol station fire.

Cause of Petrol Station Fires

So what did set off those 243 petrol station fires? Most of the time, static electricity was the culprit.

We have all seen or felt a spark from clothing. If you are wearing synthetic clothes in the dryness of winter, and are sliding in and out of the car, across the synthetic material of the car seat, then you can build up a big static charge. Then, if the earthing wire on the petrol hose is broken, when you touch the metal nozzle of the petrol hose to the metal neck of the petrol tank, you can discharge a visible spark. If you are very unlucky, the petrol vapour around the open petrol tank is in the range of 2–8% by volume. If you are extremely unlucky, the spark happens in a ball of this petrol vapour, which could explode. This has happened.

From the static electricity point of view, filling up a small fuel drum (either metal or plastic) on the back of a pick-up truck is even more dangerous. The friction between the truck and the container can build up enough energy to generate a static electricity spark. This has also happened.

Why the Petrol Station Warnings?

The phone companies post warnings about using mobile phones in petrol stations for two reasons.

First, mobile phones are not designed with 'Intrinsic Safety' to make them able to operate safely in truly hazardous inflammable vapour situations. Second, mobile phone manufacturers are afraid of legal liability, despite all the evidence showing that mobile phones have never caused a fire in a petrol station.

So overall, the mobile-phone/petrol-station-fire myth is just endless chatter generating a whole lot of static.

New York Static Electricity

In the late 1970s, I was doing research into picking up electrical signals from the human retina (this was to diagnose certain eye diseases, such as Retinitis Pigmentosa). I spent three months working on this at the Columbia Presbyterian Physicians and Surgeons Hospital in New York. I stayed in the 13-storey nurses home. It was winter, and very dry.

In the mornings, at the elevators, everybody would wait for someone else to be the first to reach out and touch the metal elevator call button. The reason was that we had all built up lots of static electricity just by walking down the corridor from our rooms, and we would generate a painful 2 cm electrical spark as we reached out to the metal elevator call button.

I always wore T-shirts during my stay there. And at the end of each day, when I went to my tiny room, I would take off my T-shirt and throw it onto the bed. The static electricity would keep it from collapsing for about 15 minutes. I didn't have a TV, so it gave me lots of free entertainment watching it slowly collapse as the static electricity drained off.

References

Jennings, Bob, 'Big bang theory', *Sydney Morning Herald*, 30 December 2005, p 4.

Mikkelson, Barbara and David P., 'Fuelish pleasures', 12 November 2006, http://www.snopes.com/autos/hazards/gasvapor.asp.

Schwartz, Ephraim, 'Mobile battery problems explode: experts ponder alternatives to batteries that have caused fire in notebooks, cell phones', *PC World*, 22 December 2003.

Suzuki, Hiroshi and Eki, Yoshinori, 'Nokia voluntarily recalls 46 million cellphone batteries', *Washington Post*, 15 August 2007.

Virki, Tarmo, 'Nokia warns consumers of battery overheating risks', *Washington Post*, 15 August 2007.

Exploding Car

(Auto ignition)

An integral part of many Hollywood movies is the gratuitous car chase. This is a way of padding out the movie, without actually having to write additional intelligent script, or advance the plot. An important part of the car chase is the car exploding as soon as it runs into another vehicle or goes over a conveniently placed cliff. In fact, the opposite is true — it is surprisingly difficult to get a petrol tank to explode and blow up a car.

Petrol 101

The liquid which is called 'petrol' in the UK and Australia is known as 'gasoline' in the USA. The word 'petrol' originally referred to the oil that came out of the ground. The term was first used in 1892 to refer to the refined liquid that you can put into an internal combustion engine. In the early days, before petrol stations existed, it was sold from chemists in bottles. It was used as a dry-cleaning fluid to remove oil stains from clothes, and to treat human hair against lice and lice eggs.

Water is a liquid made from a single chemical, H_2O.

Petrol is completely different. It's made from many different liquids, and the ratio of these constituent liquids varies widely depending on various factors. Volatility — the ability of a substance to change from a liquid into a vapour — is one of the many factors. In a cold climate, the petrol should be highly volatile, so that the engine will be easy to start. However, in a hot climate, if the petrol is too volatile, it can turn into a vapour while inside the pipes carrying the petrol from the fuel tank to the petrol pump. The pump cannot pump vapour, so the engine stops — this is known as 'vapour lock'.

LIGhts, CAMЕrA, BOOM

An important part of a movie car chase scene is the car exploding as soon as it runs into another vehicle, or goes over a conveniently placed cliff. In fact, the opposite is true – it is surprisingly difficult to get a petrol tank to explode and blow up a car.

Petrol, the liquid, will not burn.
The oxygen in the atmosphere can't get at enough molecules in the petrol to react with them and provide a fast chemical reaction. But the vapour is 'thin' enough to spread widely over a large volume of air and reach lots of oxygen. So what burns is the vapour that comes off the petrol.

Petrol can be made from toluene (up to 35% by volume), xylene (up to 25%), methyl tertiary butyl ether, or MTBE (up to 18%), trimethylbenzene (up to 7%), benzene (up to 5%), naphthalene (up to 1%), and ten or more other ingredients. To look at it another way, petrol is mainly a complicated blend of paraffins, naphthenes and olefins. Of course, alcohol, detergents, anti-corrosives, combustion improvers, reducers of internal carbon build-up, octane improvers and lubricants can also be added.

The ratio of the various chemicals depends on climate, the particular oil refinery and its capabilities, the needs of the consumers, local laws (e.g. the percentage of ethanol that must be added), and so on.

Hydrocarbons

The liquids that make up petrol have one thing in common. They contain hydrogen and carbon — in other words, they are hydrocarbons.

As far as the oil industry is concerned, the lovely thing about hydrocarbons is that they burn, giving off energy.

The hydrogen (H) in the hydrocarbon burns with oxygen (O) to give water (H_2O) and lots of energy.

$$2H_2 + O_2 \rightarrow 2\,H_2O + energy$$

The carbon (C) in the hydrocarbon burns with oxygen (O) to give carbon dioxide (CO_2) and lots of energy.

$$C + O_2 \rightarrow CO_2 + energy$$

When oil comes out of the ground, it contains lots of different hydrocarbon molecules — some of them with hundreds of carbon

hydrocarbons

The liquids that make up petrol have one thing in common.
They contain hydrogen and carbon – in other words, they are hydrocarbons.
As far as the oil industry is concerned, the lovely thing about hydrocarbons
is that they burn, giving off energy.
The hydrogen (H) in the hydrocarbon burns with oxygen (O) in the air
to give water (H_2O), and lots of energy.
The carbon (C) in the hydrocarbon burns with oxygen (O) in the air
to give carbon dioxide (CO_2), and lots of energy.

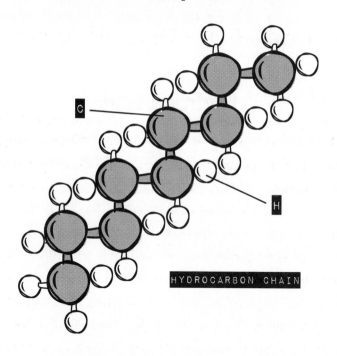

HYDROCARBON CHAIN

Hydrocarbons consist of a 'backbone' or 'skeleton'
composed of carbon and hydrogen.

atoms all joined together in a long chain. The good thing about long hydrocarbons is that they give up lots of energy. The bad thing is that long hydrocarbons are hard to start burning. Therefore, in an oil refinery the long hydrocarbons that come out of the ground are broken down into smaller hydrocarbons for your petrol tank.

In petrol, most of the hydrocarbon molecules that burn easily have between 4 and 12 carbon atoms. This range gives a good mix of easy burning and lots of energy.

Liquid Petrol Does Not Burn

Now here's the tricky part.

Petrol, the liquid, will not burn.

The oxygen in the atmosphere cannot get at enough molecules in the petrol to react with them and provide a fast chemical reaction. But the petrol vapour is 'thin' enough to spread widely over a large volume of air and reach lots of oxygen. So what burns is the vapour that comes off the petrol.

And now it gets even more tricky.

If you fill the cabin of a car entirely with petrol vapour, it won't burn — because while there's a lot of fuel, there's no oxygen to burn the fuel. So petrol vapour at 100% concentration won't burn.

Suppose you go to the other extreme and fill the cabin of the car with 0% petrol vapour and 100% air. Obviously, it won't burn, because there's no fuel.

But there is a percentage at which petrol vapour will burn, somewhere between 0% and 100%.

In most cases, in most climates, petrol vapour will burn only when it makes up between 2% and 8% of the volume, with the air making up the rest. (The exact concentration varies — other sources quote 1–6%.)

It's not that easy to get petrol vapour in a range of between 2% and 8%. This means that exploding fuel tanks are not very common.

Pinto Burned Too Well

In today's cars, the petrol tank is usually housed deep between strong lumps of steel, that are also structural members of the car. They protect the petrol tank in the event of a collision.

But one particular small 1970s American car, the Pinto, suffered from two very bad design faults. As a result, it could burst into flames when hit from behind.

First, the pipe that joined the petrol cap to the petrol tank would easily tear loose in a rear-end collision. If the Pinto were to tip over, raw petrol could pour onto the ground from the open tank.

Second, the petrol tank was immediately behind the differential — that big 'pumpkin' of metal in the middle of the back axle. The distance between the rear bumper bar and the fuel tank was only about 20 cm. Unfortunately, the rear bumper had no structural integrity and was just an ornament. In a rear-end collision, the petrol tank would get squashed against the differential, and could split open. Again, this meant that liquid petrol could spill out onto the ground.

(It didn't help that the body of the Pinto was poorly reinforced. In many accidents the doors jammed shut, making the Pinto a death trap.)

All that was needed for a fire was a spark — from bare electrical wires, or from metal parts scraping on the road, or against each other. If a spark were to occur where the petrol vapour level was between 2 and 8%, the vapour would ignite and explode.

According to the news media, about 500 people died, and another 400 were badly burnt, as a result of petrol fires caused by

Squealing Tyres

Let me get my Cranky Complaint about tyres-squealing-on-dirt off my chest.

You are watching a movie, and now it's time for the chase sequence. The cars head onto a dirt road. But even though it's a dirt road, the car tyres give off a squealing sound! Car tyres squeal only when they are being dragged across some solid surface such as bitumen or concrete, and tiny fragments of rubber are torn off the tyre. If no rubber fragments are torn off, there are no squealing sounds. On a dirt surface, the tyres simply slide across the dirt – there's no squealing sound.

You can blame it all on Jack Donovan Foley (1891–1967). He developed many of the sound effect techniques used in today's movies. At the end of a movie, in the credits, look out for 'Foley Sound'. These are the people (the 'Foley artists') who add sound to movies. Most Bollywood movies and many Italian movies are shot without any live sound being recorded at the time of filming – Foley artists add the sound later. Foley artists each have their own special individual armamentarium of apparati to make special sounds, e.g. watermelons or bamboo to make the sound of a fistfight more dramatic. They have a huge collection of surfaces and female shoes, so they can add, for example, the sound of a pair of stilettos walking across a variety of floor surfaces. And they will flap a pair of gloves to give a very good approximation of the sound of flapping wings.

They are also the dudes who unnecessarily add in the sound of squealing tyres to a car chase on dirt.

rear-end collisions in Pintos. However, according to a more sober analysis by the lawyer Gary T. Schwartz in the *Rutgers Law Review*, the Pinto was typical of similar cars of the time (1970s), which were all pretty 'unsafe' when compared to today's cars. He also argued that the number of deaths was closer to 27 than to 500.

Cars Hard to Ignite

However, the Pinto was a very unusual case. In general, cars very rarely catch on fire.

So how do they make movie cars burst into flame?

One popular method is to ignite some dynamite inside a small waterbed full of petrol on the back seat of the car. The first explosion of dynamite scatters the petrol in all directions, so that at least some of it is in the desired 2–8% level. Almost immediately, a second explosion makes sure that it burns, if burning hadn't already started with the first explosion.

It's lucky for us that, unlike in Hollywood movies, cars do not burst into flames as soon as the wheels leave the ground. Think of how difficult it would be for your mechanic to service your car, if it burst into flames every time it was being lifted off the ground with the hydraulic hoist.

If cars did burst into flame at the slightest bump, imagine how careful you would have to be with shopping trolleys in the supermarket parking lot ...

References

Donie, Mark, 'Pinto Madness', *Mother Jones*, 1 September 1977.
Schwartz, Gary T., 'The Myth of the Ford Pinto Case', *Rutgers Law Review*, Vol 43, 1991, pp 1013–1068.

GraPeFruit Juice And Drugs

(C the Truth)

Grapefruit juice sounds like the kind of stuff that is unquestionably healthy. At the very least, it must contain vitamin C, which is surely a good thing.

True, but what most people don't know is that grapefruit juice can interfere with some common medications.

Grapefruit 101

The grapefruit belongs to the citrus family. A mature tree can grow as high as 6 m, and produce up to 600 kg of fruit each year. At approximately 100–150 mm in diameter, this lemon-yellow fruit is larger than an orange. The pulp is usually a light yellow in colour, but can be pink or red. Like all citrus fruit, it has an acidic taste.

The grapefruit was first documented in 1750 by the Reverend Griffith Hughes as coming from Barbados in the Caribbean. It was taken to Florida in 1823 for further cultivation. In 1929, after a bit of crossbreeding, a grapefruit variety called the Ruby Red became very popular in the USA. Over the years, the grapefruit was crossbred to produce the orlando tangelo, the minneola and the sweetie (oroblanco). Today, the USA (with a production of one million tonnes) and China (with half a million tonnes) account for about half the world's annual production.

Accidental Discovery — 1

The interactions of grapefruit juice with some medications first came to the attention of the medical community in 1991 with the publication of a paper in the prestigious medical journal *The Lancet*. Written by Dr David G. Bailey, from Ontario in Canada, the paper opens with three dry words, 'A chance finding', and then goes on to describe, in very academic language, that grapefruit juice can increase the levels of a certain drug in the blood. Those three words, 'A chance finding', do not even hint at the real story.

In their study, Dr Bailey and his fellow researchers wanted to find out whether alcohol had any effect on a new blood pressure drug called felodipine. But they wanted to keep the presence of the alcohol hidden from the volunteers.

Dr Bailey was given the job of disguising the strong burning taste of the pure alcohol. He was probably not the best person to ask, as he was both a non-drinker and an athlete — in fact, he was the first Canadian to run the four-minute mile. He and his wife spent the Friday night before the study began rummaging through the pantry and the fridge. He later said, 'The only thing that covered the taste [of the alcohol] was grapefruit juice.'

So, thinking that grapefruit juice was inert as far as their study was concerned, they used it to mask the taste of the alcohol. Their study found that alcohol did not interact with the blood pressure drug felodipine.

the Bitter truth ABOut GraPeFruit

Grapefruit juice has long been accepted as being unquestionably healthy.
Common belief asserts it is rich in vitamin C, surely a good thing.
This is true – however, the grapefruit has a dark side.
Grapefruit juice can interfere with some common medications.

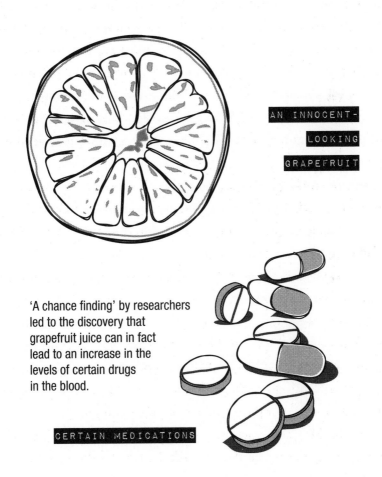

AN INNOCENT-
LOOKING
GRAPEFRUIT

'A chance finding' by researchers
led to the discovery that
grapefruit juice can in fact
lead to an increase in the
levels of certain drugs
in the blood.

CERTAIN MEDICATIONS

Accidental Discovery — 2

However, they also discovered something weird — the drug levels in the blood of the volunteers were three times higher than expected!

The researchers contacted the drug company that supplied them, and asked if they had accidentally labelled 20 mg tablets as being 5 mg tablets. But an analysis of the tablets found them to contain, as advertised, 5 mg of felodipine.

So Dr Bailey did a mini-study on himself. The first day, he took felodipine with water, and sent a blood sample off for analysis. The second day, he took felodipine with grapefruit juice and, again, sent off a blood sample.

His body told him that his blood levels of the blood pressure drug were sky-high, long before the results came back. He felt very light-headed and then actually fainted. This was a very powerful indication that his blood pressure was much too low, thanks to high levels of the felodipine.

This was the very first recorded instance of a pharmacokinetic interaction between a citrus juice and a drug.

But it seems impossible. Grapefruit does not contain any felodipine. Your body does not make the drug felodipine. So where does the extra felodipine come from?

How Does It Work?

The mechanisms by which grapefruit juice increases the blood levels of certain drugs are complicated, and have taken many years to understand. In this case, grapefruit juice increased the oral absorption of the felodipine.

A rough analogy might be a stupid radio station promotion, in which a million dollars is dumped into a fast-flowing stream. You can keep all the money that you can scoop out of the

More Technical Explanation

Enzymes are chemicals that kick certain chemical reactions along.

Cells in the wall of the human gut – known as apical enterocytes – contain many, many enzymes. A specific subfamily of the cytochrome P450 enzymes is especially relevant, if you have grapefruit juice in your gut and take certain medications.

These cytochrome P450 enzymes normally break down, or metabolise, certain drugs such as nifedipine, felodipine, nimodipine, cyclosporin and midazolam. They might destroy over half of the drug while it's in your gut. This means that under normal conditions, these cytochrome P450 enzymes lead to fairly low levels of these drugs being available for absorption into the bloodstream.

But grapefruit inhibits or reduces the activity of these destructive enzymes, so they work more slowly. The enzymes now don't do a very good job of breaking down the drugs that you swallow. As a result, more of these drugs are available to be absorbed into the bloodstream.

If you really want more technical details, the specific subfamily is cytochrome P450 3A4 (CYP3A4). This means that grapefruit affects only those drugs that are metabolised by cytochrome P450 3A4 (CYP3A4). It turns out that in our society, the elderly are the ones most likely to take medications that are metabolised by cytochrome P450 3A4 (CYP3A4).

And if you want to get really technical, the active chemicals in the grapefruit that do the inhibiting are called 'furanocoumarins'. There may be other chemicals that also do the inhibiting, but we haven't discovered them yet.

stream — but the radio station has given you only a tiny teaspoon to do the scooping. You could collect more banknotes if you used a butterfly net.

In a similar way, the medication enters at your mouth and leaves via the 'other end' into your toilet bowl. Only a small amount leaves your gut and enters your bloodstream. With some drugs, however, grapefruit juice increases how much gets absorbed (or 'scooped') into your bloodstream.

In other words, you swallow a certain dose of the drug (say, 5 mg). But only (say) 0.5 mg actually makes its way from the gut into the bloodstream. The remaining 4.5 mg goes out through the S-bend and into the sewer.

But with some drugs, the presence of grapefruit juice in the gut increases the quantity of drug that is absorbed into the bloodstream.

Drugs Go Up

In addition to the blood pressure drugs in the felodipine group, grapefruit alters the natural absorption of many other drugs. In fact, when taking these medications, grapefruit juice can sometimes send a person's blood levels of the drug dangerously high. These medications include some blood pressure drugs, antihistamines, hormones, immunosuppressives, antivirals, anticonvulsants, statins (for cholesterol), sedatives, opiates, antidepressants of the SSRI variety, and even Viagra (causing painful erection, low blood pressure and impaired vision).

And we have found other fruits (e.g. limes, Seville oranges and sometimes even apples) that can increase the levels of some drugs in your body.

However, just to show how complicated the body is, while double-strength grapefruit juice tripled the blood levels of felodipine, some varieties of orange juice had no effect at all.

We can't really use this effect to reliably increase medication levels in people. One reason is that this effect is very strong in some people and very weak in others. Another reason is that grapefruit varies enormously in its strength, from one variety to the next, from one farm to the next, from one fruit juice manufacturer to the next, from one batch to the next, and so on.

Drugs Go Down

And, of course, because the human body is so complicated, drug levels in the blood can sometimes decrease when different drugs and fruit are mixed.

In August 2008 our hero, Dr David Bailey (now a Professor of Clinical Pharmacology), announced that all the aforementioned fruits (i.e. grapefruit, limes, Seville Oranges and apples) can sometimes decrease the blood levels of some other medications.

In this case, a different chemical in grapefruit works via a different pathway. The active ingredient is called 'naringin'. It seems to block an important drug uptake transporter, called 'OATP1A2'. This carries drugs from the small intestine to the bloodstream. So if you block this transporter, you reduce the quantity of medication that gets carried into the bloodstream.

Various drugs have their blood concentrations lowered if you take them with the juice of grapefruit, orange and apple. These drugs include etoposide (an anti-cancer drug), certain beta blockers used to treat high blood pressure and prevent heart attacks (such as atenolol, celipropol and talinolol), and some antibiotics (ciprofloxacin, levofloxacin and itraconazole).

In oranges, the active chemical that interferes with the transporter, OATP1A2, is 'hesperidin'. But the active chemical in apples that does the interfering has not yet been identified.

What to Do?

Because this effect happens in the gut, it works only with medications that you swallow. Medications that are injected into the bloodstream or muscles bypass the gut, and are therefore not affected by any grapefruit in your diet.

The lesson here is to check with your doctor or pharmacist about possible interactions with your medications — including food. After all, many medications are taken at breakfast, and that's when grapefruit juice might also be taken. The journal *Australian Adverse Drug Reactions Bulletin* advises, 'Separate grapefruit juice and medication by a minimum of two hours.'

And who knows? One day soon you may find your local grocer putting health warning stickers on fruit …

A Happy Reader

This is an email sent to me by a Happy Reader.

Dear Dr Kruszelnicki,

In your article 'Is grapefruit juice safe?' in the 'Good Weekend' of 20 September 2008 you wrote about the interaction of grapefruit juice with certain medications.

I am 82 years old and have been having a glass of grapefruit juice with my breakfast for the last 30 years. For the last 5 years I have been on Nexium for my hiatus hernia, 20 mg per day.

For the last 2 to 3 years I have developed a most irritating clogged throat every day after breakfast, and it usually lasts for most of the morning and often till later in the day.

Having read your article I thought I ought to try a different juice for breakfast on the days when I take the

Nexium – I am now only taking 1 pill every other day – with dramatic results.

The ghastly rasping cough has just about vanished, and as a consequence I am feeling much better. I thought the throat irritation would ultimately end in throat cancer and was really worried. Thank you very much for the information and I am truly grateful for the help and advice you gave in your column.

Best wishes,

. . .

References

Bailey, David G., et al., 'Grapefruit juice–drug interactions', *British Journal of Clinical Pharmacology*, August 1998, Vol 46, No 2, pp 101–110.

Bailey, David G., et al., 'Interaction of citrus juices with felodipine and nifedipine,' *The Lancet*, 2 February 1991, pp 268–269.

Bakalar, Nicholas, 'Experts reveal the secret powers of grapefruit juice', *The New York Times*, 21 March 2006.

Garg, Santosh K., et al., 'Effect of grapefruit juice on carbamazepine bioavailability in patients with epilepsy', *Clinical Pharmacology & Therapeutics*, September 1998, pp 286–288.

Paine, Mary F., et al., 'A furanocoumarin-free grapefruit juice established furanocoumarins as the mediators of the grapefruit juice–felodipine interaction', *American Journal of Clinical Nutrition*, May 2006, Vol 83, No 5, pp 1097–1105.

GreenLANd GreenhOuse

The claim by the Climate Change Sceptics is, at face value, kind of reasonable. About 1,000 years ago, they say, the world's climate was a lot warmer. After all, the Vikings had colonies in Greenland, which must have been given that name because it was green. Then, as the climate changed and Greenland got cold and covered with ice, the Viking colonies died out.

And now it's warming up again? Well, argue the Climate Change Sceptics, why should we worry, because the Greenland story is proof that the world's climate is constantly changing.

Viking

There's a bit of controversy about the origin of the word 'Viking'.

One claim is that it means a man from the Vik, a huge bay that lies between the mouth of the Göta River in Sweden and Cape Lindesnes in Norway.

But another claim is that it comes from the word *vikingr*, which means 'pirate' in an early Scandinavian language.

Yet another claim is that it comes from the old English word *wic*, meaning 'a fortified trade settlement'.

And yet another claim is that 'viking' comes from the Old Norse verb *vika*, meaning 'to go off'.

It's Not That Simple

Any discussion about Climate Change is complicated. Partly because climate is complicated. Partly because there are natural changes in the climate going on anyhow. And partly because human beings are changing the climate by dumping Greenhouse Gases into the atmosphere.

Whenever you try to make a story easy to understand, there is also the danger of making the story inaccurate.

For example, this story — of Norse people settling Greenland, but then dying when the world cooled down — is a good example of a story that is both simple and wrong.

The real story is actually quite messy, and very interesting.

The Real Story

Eric the Red (or Erik Thorvaldsson), who lived from c. 950–c.1003 AD, was the first Norseman to set up permanent colonies in Greenland.

His parents had violent tendencies. They had to flee Norway and move to western Iceland because of 'some killing'. Unfortunately, their son, Eric the Red, also had a tendency to get into arguments and kill people. After three such fights and subsequent deaths, he was exiled from Iceland around the year 982 for three years.

He had heard tales of an uninhabited country about 800 km to the west. Two other sailors had been to this country over the previous century. Gunnbjorn Ulfsson (or Ulf-Krakuson) had been driven there by strong winds, while Snaebjorn Glati had tried to colonise this country, but failed.

Eric's parents were not welcome in Norway, and he was not welcome in Iceland. So he sailed west and found the uninhabited country. He spent the three years of his exile exploring the fairly inhospitable place. At that time, in 985 AD, the climate in Greenland was roughly similar to what it is today. So the landscape was very similar to what it is today — about 80% ice, 19% bare rock, and just 1% green. But he did find a few locations, at the head of long fjords, that were relatively comfortable in the short summer.

After his three years of exile were up, he returned to Iceland. He realised that he could be a leader in this new country — all he needed was followers. So he called the new land 'Greenland'. This was because, according to the *Saga of Eric the Red*, 'people would be more attracted to go there if it had a favourable name'.

There was nothing particularly green about Greenland — this was just Creative Advertising on the part of Eric the Red. His tales of this fertile land succeeded — it certainly helped that there had been a recent famine in Iceland — and he attracted about 500 settlers. They all set off in a fleet of 25 Viking longboats to colonise Greenland. Only 14 of the longboats arrived — the others were lost at sea, or turned back.

Colonising Greenland

Once the colonising fleet arrived, they realised that their new home wasn't quite as lovely as Eric had told them.

They colonised two main settlements.

The larger one was the Eastern Settlement. Despite its name, it was virtually at the southern tip of Greenland (only 50 km to its west). At its peak in around 1126 AD, it had '190 small farms, 12 parish churches, a cathedral, an Augustinian monastery and a Benedictine nunnery'. The peak population was about 2,000 to 4,000 inhabitants.

The smaller one was the Western Settlement. It was situated about 550 km northwest of the Eastern Settlement, and so it was both closer to the North Pole and more inhospitable in winter.

At its peak population of about 1,000 inhabitants, it had '90 farms and 4 churches'.

At first, the colonists flourished in this virgin land. From time to time, more colonists arrived from Iceland. Unfortunately, one group of immigrants who arrived in 1002 AD brought a particularly nasty epidemic with them. It killed many colonists, including Eric the Red himself in 1003 AD.

King Trick

In the 11th century, the Viking King Magnus Barelegs used the lightness of his beautiful longships to trick the King of Scotland.

The King of Scotland had made a treaty with King Magnus, that Magnus could have all of the land that he could sail his ship around. The King of Scotland had realised that there was no point in trying to hang onto all the islands off the Scottish coast, because he could not defend them.

In Scotland, the Kintyre Peninsula is 65 km long, with a very narrow neck. So King Magnus sailed up to this narrow neck, and while sitting at the rudder of his light but strong dragon ship, was dragged across the narrow strip of land. Legally and cunningly, he claimed the Peninsula of Kintyre.

Problems — 1

The colonists also had to contend with hostile locals, the Inuit. In one single battle, the Norse settlers lost 2% of the adult males. In today's terms, that would equate to 100,000 Australian male deaths.

They also had major problems with trade. In 1349–1350, the Black Death swept through Norway, their major and only legal

GrEENLANd, you're wARMING to It

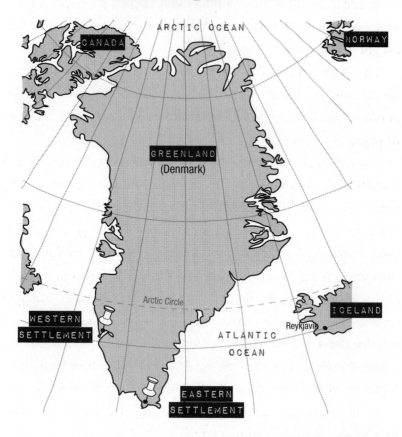

Once the colonising fleet arrived in Greenland, they realised that their
new home wasn't quite as lovely as they had been told.
They colonised two main settlements.
The larger one was the Eastern Settlement. Despite its name, it was virtually
at the southern tip of Greenland (only 50 kilometres to its west).
At its peak around 1126 AD, it had '190 small farms, 12 parish churches,
a cathedral, an Augustinian monastery and a Benedictine nunnery'.
The peak population was around 2,000 to 4,000 inhabitants.

trading partner. It killed about half the Norwegian population. Norway virtually abandoned the colonists, the last official Norwegian ship visiting in 1368. From 1368 until the ultimate downfall of the colonies around 1450, only four other ships visited — in 1381, 1382, 1385 and 1406. It was illegal for private ships to visit, so they each claimed to have been blown off course and caught in heavy fog.

The Greenlanders also created major environmental problems for themselves. Only 1% of the landscape was green. The tiny amounts of soil that were present had been built up over millions of years.

The colonists didn't treat their new home gently — they caused massive soil erosion through a combination of overgrazing, tree lopping for ships, pasture and firewood, and reckless management. For example, to cover the roof and walls of one large house, they used some four hectares of turf, which could otherwise have been used for growing crops or raising livestock. The first settlers had a diet that was 80% based on land agriculture (which was very environmentally costly), and only 20% came from the surrounding sea. By the 1300s, when they were on their last legs, they had changed their diet so that about 65% of it came from the ocean. However, by this time, their numbers were too small to survive.

By the end, they were reduced to eating the flesh off the tiny foot bones of rabbits and small birds.

Problems — 2

And yes, besides the very hostile neighbours and the self-inflicted environmental problems, the climate did change after the colonists arrived in 985 AD. There were several sets of cold years in the 1300s, followed by the Little Ice Age in the 1400s. This caused many ocean icebergs, which greatly hampered ocean travel.

Ice core analyses tell us that between 800 and 1300 AD, the climate in Greenland was similar to what it is today, or perhaps slightly warmer. This period is called the Medieval Warm Period. According to Jared Diamond, author of *Collapse: How Societies Choose to Fail or Survive*, 'Around 1300 though, the climate in the North Atlantic began to get cooler and more variable from year to year, ushering in a cold period termed the Little Ice Age that lasted into the 1800s. By around 1420, the Little Ice Age was in full swing, and the increased summer drift ice between Greenland, Iceland and Norway ended ship communication between the Greenland Norse and the outside world.'

The last inhabitants of the more northern settlement (the Western Settlement) died around 1350 AD. A traveller from the Eastern Settlement visited it and found it to be empty of life.

The last records that we have of the Eastern Settlement are from Thorstein Olafsson, the captain of the ship that visited in 1406. He appeared to be content to stay there for four years. He reported three events — witchcraft, insanity and a marriage. In 1407, a man was burnt at the stake for using witchcraft to attempt the seduction of a woman named Steinunn. Then Steinunn went insane. Finally, in 1408, Captain Olafsson married a Greenland woman. He left Greenland in 1410.

So yes, the Norse colonists had to contend with Climate Change. But previous cold snaps before the 1300s had not forced them to extinction, and some warm periods in the 1400s did not save them.

Survival

The colonists also had to deal with aggressive neighbours, loss of trade, environmental problems so huge that they could not feed themselves, and poor responses to those problems (e.g. eating beef instead of fish). In fact, it's amazing that they survived so long.

Even today, Greenland survives only with massive subsidies from Denmark, and from fishing licence payments. The true story of the Greenland colonists is far more complicated than 'it got cold and they died'. After all, the Inuit not only survived during this entire period, but also flourished, and are still there today. 'When later European explorers began visiting Greenland in the late 1500s, they were immediately amazed at the speed and maneuverability of kayaks and commented on the Inuit appearing to be half fish, darting around in the water much faster than any European boat could travel.'

So it was not just the changing climate that booted the Norse out of Greenland.

There's a lot to be said for local knowledge — and the joy of fishing.

Dragon Ships

A medieval prayer from the Middle Ages says: 'From the fury of the Norsemen, good Lord deliver us.'

The Norsemen, or Vikings, had a terrible reputation. They got their money from exorbitant taxes, tributes, trade, outright extortion, daylight robbery and plain old piracy. At their peak, their power extended across all of Scotland, Ireland and England, through Europe, and deep into the Mediterranean Sea. And they did it all thanks to the Viking longship – the dreaded dragon ship.

These magnificent dragon ships could cross oceans, land on beaches and sail up rivers. They didn't suddenly spring into existence – they were the peak of the evolution of 6,000 years of shipbuilding.

The evolution began with Scandinavian Stone Age dugout canoes, around 5,000 BC. The Stone Age boatwrights used flint tools to scrape out the inside of soft, long-lasting linden trees. They were so skilful, even 7,000 years ago, that they could make a canoe with a wall only 2 cm thick. These canoes, which measured up to 10 m in length, were used for catching whales – and winning wars.

About 5,000 years ago, the boatwrights along the banks of the Åmose River in Denmark came up with a new trick. They made a row of holes along the upper edges of the sideboards of their canoes. Then they carved planks with matching holes, and tied them onto the side walls of their dugout. This increased the distance between the water and the top of the hull. These boats travelled safely to Norway and Sweden.

During the Bronze Age (from 2,000 BC to 500 BC), some of the features of the classic Viking ship appeared – such as the posts at each end, crowned with the heads of animals, snakes or dragons. This high post was actually the extension of protective timbers on the pointy end of the boat.

By the time of the Iron Age (500 BC–400 AD), the prow was a major feature of the boat. It took a lot of energy to make – but it was too tall and too weak to be used as a battering ram. However, it must have had some sort of protective or stabilising effect, because Iron Age shipbuilders put one at each end of the boat.

This was the world's first real double-ended boat with wonderful engineering features.

The advantage of a double-ended warship was that it could reverse without having to turn. This could save the Norsemen's lives when they had to suddenly retreat from a superior force.

It was also higher at the ends than in the middle. This stopped water from entering the boat.

The advantage of the deeper midsection was that it gave the boat a better grip on the water during a turn. In fact, by the end of the Viking era, the keel of the dragon ship was about 30 cm deeper in the centre section of the boat than at either end. A measurement of 30 cm is almost invisible in a boat 35 m long, but the Viking shipwrights incorporated this subtle curve, because it was needed.

There were a few different styles of longships.

The small levy ships had fewer than 20 rowing benches. The local communities had to keep some in good repair, to provide warriors for the king, whenever he sent around the symbolic war arrow.

The standard longships had up to 30 rowing benches.

Later in the Viking era the so-called great ships had more than 30 rowing benches. These great ships were 35 m long, about 3 m wide, and about 1 m high from the top plank to the keel. They weren't called longships for nothing.

These dragon ships could cross an ocean, ride out a gale, cruise a river and land on any beach. They were both a troop carrier and a landing ship. They could discharge their crew of 60 armed warriors within a minute. They were definitely beautiful ships.

A song about the ship of King Harald Hardruler goes, 'As Norsemen row the serpent, the riveted [ship] down the icy stream, it is like a sight of eagle's wings'.

The dragon ships were constructed from the best materials. One recently excavated Viking longship had been made from 300-year-old trees. The planks were over 10 m long, without a single imperfection.

The Viking shipwrights would split the tree trunks in a radial pattern – like the spokes of a bicycle wheel radiating out from the centre. Splitting the timber gave greater strength than sawing it. Using planks made from radially cut timbers from the same tree meant that they were all the same strength.

The ships were made from many overlapping planks. The advantage of having planks was that it was easy to make the curves that were needed. The disadvantage was that they could leak.

But the Vikings were hardy people. According to Norse law a ship was regarded as seaworthy if the crew didn't have to bail it out more than three times in two days. Of course, the crew could decide to sail in the boat even if it was unseaworthy, but they weren't forced to.

The Viking era ran only three centuries, from 800 to 1100 AD. During this time they travelled all around Scandinavia, deep into Russia, throughout the British Isles and into Europe as far south as Spain, and then on to the Mediterranean Sea as far east as the Black Sea.

Still, they could not effectively control the larger and richer states that they had overrun. They didn't have the political experience, or the stable home society, or the wealth that was needed to build an empire. And the world itself had changed after 1100. Impregnable walls were built around city ports and navies were organised.

Soon the graceful dragon ships went the way of the beasts that they were named after. And so the magnificent fighting ships of the Vikings were replaced by prosaic cargo ships.

References

Arneborg, J., et al., 'C-14 dating and the disappearance of Norsemen from Greenland', *Europhysics News*, March 2003.

Diamond, Jared, *Collapse: How Societies Choose to Fail or Survive*, Camberwell, Victoria: Penguin, 2005, pp 179–276.

FOur-wheeL Drive Safety

A while ago, I was talking to a bunch of school kids after giving a fun/motivational science talk. At the time, my elder daughter was learning to drive, and so I asked them who was learning to drive, and in what type of vehicle. A few of them said they were learning in four-wheel drives (4WDs) — and they had been told that 4WDs were safer than standard passenger cars.

They were soooooo wrong. Four-wheel drive vehicles are not always safer, and in some cases are less safe.

The students and I ended up having a very long discussion, especially in light of the fact that 4WDs are popular family cars.

But first, what is a 4WD?

4WD, SUV, or What?

Back in the Old Days (before the arrival of the Range Rover in 1970), a 4WD was a fairly crude vehicle that fed power to both the front and rear axles. Assuming that there was a good road surface and no wheel spin, this gave you all four wheels driving the vehicle forward — hence the name four-wheel drive. It also sat higher than an average sedan. In the USA, the equivalent was a sports utility vehicle or SUV. Early 4WDs were utilitarian and were mainly used for agricultural purposes and in the military.

Then the luxury Range Rover arrived on the scene. It had a unique suspension, with long travel and high compliance on each wheel. In the earlier 4WDs the suspension was quite stiff, and each wheel moved up and down only a short distance when you went over rough ground. But in the Range Rover the suspension was quite floppy, and each wheel moved a larger distance up and down. This made it very comfortable to travel in. Surprisingly for the adherents of the old suspension, the Range Rover was also extremely capable in Outback conditions. (However, it had only a short range, thanks to its rather thirsty petrol engine.)

Even though the term 4WD (or SUV) included comfortable and luxury vehicles, they were all higher than the standard passenger car. They had, thanks to their greater ground clearance, the capability to travel in the Australian Outback.

But then the definition of a 4WD became complicated by the insertion of a four-wheel drive system into otherwise standard passenger cars. These vehicles rode at the same height as other sedans, but the drive train now operated all four wheels. This was to give superior traction in slippery conditions.

But for this story, when I say 4WD, I mean the vehicles that definitely ride higher than the average sedan.

There are many arguments to consider in this complicated issue of car safety, so let's run through them one at a time.

Increased Height

Thanks to improved technology, most 4WDs no longer feel like a truck to drive. In many cases, they drive almost like a regular car. This car-like feel lulls the inexperienced driver into a false sense of security.

Regardless of feeling a lot like a car, one problem with practically all 4WDs is that they have a higher centre of gravity.

This increased height comes from two factors. First, the wheels are usually bigger than those on a sedan, so the drive train sits a little higher. Second, the body is usually mounted higher above the drive train than in a sedan, to give extra ground clearance for rough territory.

In 2004, the US National Highway Traffic Safety Administration began putting vehicles through rollover tests. They found that 4WDs were far more likely to tip over than regular cars. And away from the laboratory, and in the specific example of rollovers associated with a road crash, SUVs are four times more likely to roll over than a conventional passenger car.

There's not a lot the manufacturers can do to compensate for this higher centre of gravity, which makes it all too easy for a 4WD to tip over when a driver inadvertently takes the vehicle out of its stable equilibrium zone, e.g. swerving to avoid an animal.

Extra Weight

Another problem with 4WDs is that they are significantly heavier than regular cars.

The extra weight increases their braking distance. It also makes them far less nimble and less manoeuvrable in tricky situations. For a good example, think of a random pair of animals (of roughly the same size, but different weights) running fast then trying to change direction rapidly — say, a hippo and a horse. I'd have my money on the horse, for pulling the quick sidestep.

4WD Higher and Side Impacts

In a front collision, there is a lot of metal between you and the outside world. But in a side collision, there is only a door, some 10 cm thick, most of which is empty space. In 2002, 9,600 passengers in the USA died in side impact collisions.

Car doors are made from a few sheets of thin metal welded together. This means they are not very good at stopping a side impact from another car. So over the last few decades, car doors have been made stronger by having an anti-intrusion bar – a thick tube of very strong steel – welded in place just below the bottom of the window.

If you (in a sedan) get hit by another sedan from the side, the anti-intrusion bar will protect you. But if you are in a sedan, and get hit by a high-riding 4WD, its bumper bar will ride over the top of the anti-intrusion bar, come through the glass window and hit you in the upper body.

The problem is inherent in the 4WD being higher than a conventional sedan.

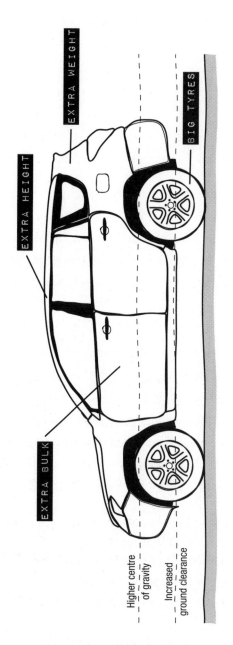

EXTRA HEIGHT

EXTRA WEIGHT

EXTRA BULK

BIG TYRES

Higher centre
of gravity

Increased
ground clearance

The BIGGER the BETTER?

There are benefits to 4WD passengers associated with being in a heavier and higher vehicle. But they are offset by the increased risk of rollovers, and the decreased manoeuvrability.

Big Fat Tyres

The big fat tyres on a 4WD are another safety problem.

When you turn the steering wheel, various metal gears, cogs and rods rotate and/or move in various directions, and after a bit of mucking around, force the metal front wheels to turn. But the metal wheel doesn't touch the road. No, there's a rubber tyre between the metal wheel and the road.

There are different types of tyres.

In Ferraris and other sporty cars, the tyre is like a skinny strip of licorice, only 5–10 cm thick from where it sits on the metal wheel to where it kisses the road, and doesn't have a lot of slop in it. Racing drivers call this a 'direct feel' — you turn the steering wheel and, almost immediately, the rubber tyre begins to change its grip on the road, and shift the car.

But in a 4WD the tyre is like a big fat cushion, some 15–20 cm thick. It needs to be this thick to absorb the shocks of the rough roads. When you turn the steering wheel, the metal front wheels begin to turn — but the big fat rubber tyre absorbs the motion. It will eventually begin to change its grip on the road, but there is a time delay. So in a tricky situation which requires some evasive manoeuvring, the vehicle is always reacting a little while after the driver has actually turned the wheel. The unfortunate driver may then turn the wheel wildly this way and that in a frantic effort to straighten up the 4WD. But because the driver is out of time with the vehicle's actual movements, the vehicle keeps swinging further to each side with each oscillation — until it goes out of control. (In the airline accident business, the investigators call this a PIO — pilot induced oscillation.)

A vehicle that insulates the driver from the 'feel' of the road is not ideal for someone learning to drive.

Airbags

I love airbags. In addition to seat belts, they are a good way to give extra protection to passengers in a car crash. (I specifically exclude children in the front seat of an airbag-equipped car. Children are likely to be injured by the rapidly expanding front airbag, because of their large head size relative to their body size, and correspondingly weaker neck muscles.)

Airbags can make the difference between life and death. In the USA in 2004, the Toyota Camry and the Honda Accord were tested in crash tests and rated for the protection that they provided to passengers, when they were hit in the side by 4WDs, SUVs and pick-up trucks. When they had the expensive optional side airbags that give head protection, they each got the highest of the four safety ratings. But the standard version of each car, without the airbags, got the lowest rating.

And here's the rub. In 2004 in the USA, only 15% of people paid extra for the Toyota Camry model with the side airbags, because it's cheaper not to have to pay for the airbags. But finally, some car manufacturers are installing the full complement of airbags in every model in their range.

Crash Safety

Finally, if there is a crash, what actually happens? Well, it depends on how the 4WD is built.

There are two main designs.

The first is the monocoque design (from the Greek *mono*, meaning 'single', and French *coque*, meaning 'shell'), in which the floor, sides and roof are a single integrated structure. Conventional cars also use this design. This kind of structure is usually integrated with crumple-zone technology, which absorbs much of the shock of a collision.

In the other design (as in most 4WDs), the body is mounted on a pair of solid rails — a chassis — and usually does not incorporate crumple-zone technology. This design does not do well when it runs into a fixed object, or into something that weighs as much as it does. It wins only when it runs into something lighter.

The ideal situation after a collision is that all of the shock should be absorbed by the car (which has given its all to protect the occupants) and that none of the shock goes to the occupants. Most 4WDs are too 'stiff' and do not absorb enough of the shock.

Safer to Not Wear Seat Belt?

Every now and then, in a discussion of seat belts, somebody will come up with a story of how they (or a friend, or a friend of a friend) were in a terrible crash, but survived only because they did not wear a seat belt, and were ejected from the car.

First, not all crashes happen near a conveniently located hill of straw or cardboard boxes upon which one can land ever so gently.

Second, US data looked at this specific situation of all occupants in rollover crashes. They found that 72% were not restrained (!), and that about half were ejected from the car. If they were restrained, only 4% were ejected. But of all of those ejected from a car, 62% were killed.

So if you are in a collision, it's safer to be wearing a seat belt, rather than not wearing a seat belt and being ejected.

The Reality

In the USA, wearing a seat belt is not always compulsory, and varies from state to state. However, wearing a seat belt when travelling in an SUV is very important, because they roll over more frequently than sedans.

A 2006 study from the Children's Hospital of Philadelphia, looked at crashes involving some 4,000 children aged between 0 and 15 years, in SUVs built in 1998, or later.

Looking at kids in rollover accidents in SUVs, if they were not wearing appropriate seat belts, 41% suffered a serious injury. This dropped to just 3% if they were wearing seat belts in an SUV rollover, and 2% if they were wearing seat belts in a passenger car rollover.

The study found that kids in SUVs have similar injury risks to those in passenger cars.

On one hand, bigger and heavier cars tend to provide more safety for their occupants. Overall, each 227 kg (500 lb) increase in weight led to a 14% decrease in injuries. One glaring exception was the case of compact extended-cab pick-up trucks — kids in the back seat suffer a five-times rate of injury increase, as compared to kids in the back seat of all other types of vehicles.

On the other hand, SUVs were twice as likely to roll over as compared to a sedan. Furthermore, children were three times as likely to be injured in a rollover if they were in an SUV.

4WDs Not Safer

Yes, there are benefits associated with being in a heavier and higher vehicle. But they are offset by the increased risk of rollovers, and decreased manoeuvrability. Overall, in terms of safety for the occupants of a 4WD, the opposing factors balance out.

Four-wheel drives are not inherently safer — their safety depends on the type of crash you're intending to have and, of course, who is behind the wheel.

The Nut Behind the Wheel

Way back in March 1899, the British journal *The Autocar* described one of the very first well-documented fatal car crashes. One critical factor in the crash was that a wheel collapsed. But at the inquest, the coroner advised the jury that the car 'appeared to be going at too rapid a pace to be safe, either for the occupants themselves, or the public'. Even back then, it was recognised that not only was the engineering of the vehicle important, so was the behaviour of the driver.

Over a million people die on the world's roads each year. Most of them are young. In the USA, about 41,000 people die in road accidents each year. In terms of road deaths per registered vehicle, in 1966 the USA was the safest in the world, but by 2000 had slipped to 13th place.

Dr Leonard Evan, who had a 33-year research career with General Motors Corporation, wrote that '. . . despite an obsessive focus on vehicle safety or arguably because of it, the U.S. ranking in the world has steadily slipped. The focus on vehicle factors – factors over which they have no control – has encouraged American drivers to regard safety as something out of their control . . . A disproportionate emphasis on vehicular factors affecting safety has distracted Americans from the importance of driver behavior.'

References

Daly, Lauren, et al., 'Risk of injury to child passengers in sport utility vehicles', *Pediatrics*, January 2006, Vol 117, No 1, pp 9–14.

Evans, Leonard, 'Traffic crashes: measures to make traffic safer are most effective when they weigh the relative importance of factors such as automotive engineering and driver behavior', *American Scientist*, May–June 2002, Vol 90, No 3, pp 244–253.

Hakim, Danny, 'Some popular SUVs fare badly in rollover tests', *The New York Times*, 8 June 2004.

Hakim, Danny, 'Struck in side, many cars fare poorly in safety test', *The New York Times*, 19 April 2004.

WhAt's thε Buzz ABOut ROyAL JεLLy?

The humble bee is essential to our society. It has been around for at least 65 million years, while honeybees go back about 10 million years. The earliest proof of honeybees' importance to us dates back to 13,000 years ago. That's when cave paintings show human beings gathering honey from hives.

With today's agriculture, bees are even more important. Bees pollinate crops for us, and so they are responsible for one out of every three mouthfuls of food that we eat.

Bees live (of course) in beehives. Despite her name, the queen bee doesn't run the hive — she is its reproductive slave. She is the mother of all the bees in the hive.

Even though most of us are not insect specialists, we've probably heard of the truly amazing substance called royal jelly that can turn regular baby bees (larvae) that are otherwise destined to become worker bees into queen bees.

Now there are people who want you to believe that what's good for the goose is good for the gander — or, in this case, that what's good for the bees is good for the people. And, therefore, they reckon that you should buy royal jelly.

Royal jelly does perform amazing makeovers on bee larvae (it seems to do this via fooling around with the DNA of the larvae). But this does not make royal jelly some kind of super health food for human beings.

Bees Work for Us

In the USA, some 90 crops depend almost entirely on the honeybee for pollination. The value of this pollination has been estimated to be around US$19 billion per year. Each year in the USA, a million beehives are shuttled cross-country to pollinate the almonds in California in February, the apple orchards of Washington in March, and so on. Even Australian bees are exported to California to help in the pollination of alfalfa, apples, almonds, etc. And each year, some one million bee colonies are spread across the fields. They are roughly distributed at about 250 colonies per square kilometre of apple orchards, and double that for almond orchards.

Now the bee is probably the first insect that springs to mind when you think about an insect having an economic impact on Western society. Silkworms probably run a close second, with the silk they make. Of course, other insects help decompose all kinds of organic matter so that they, and other creatures, can recycle it. Some insects produce stuff we use, such as 'lac' from the lac insects which is used as a resin or lacquer for violins, or cochineal (a scarlet dye used to colour food, which is derived from the dried bodies of the female scale insect). And, of course, insects eat pests, and many organic farmers and home gardeners use mantids, ladybird beetles and the like to control other critters.

The bee is probably the only creature (other than the cow) whose 'secretion' we regularly eat or drink – and who doesn't like honey? To make just one kilogram of this secretion (honey)? bees have to travel a distance equal to ten loops around the planet and visit ten million flowers to get the nectar.

And they are one of the very few insects that appear in advertisements in a flattering light.

The Claims

Royal jelly is Big Business, and the marketing claims about it are big as well.

It's been claimed to fix appetite (too much or too little), blood pressure (too high or too low), mental state (depression or overstimulation), sexual desire (any kind), wrinkles, influenza, enfeeblement and, of course, ageing. Cellulite, heart disease and stroke are also included in the list of illnesses that can be cured. The immune system can be 'boosted', while skin disorders and bacterial and viral infections can be tamed. And just to cover all possibilities, it could cure chronic and incurable disorders.

As a skin product, it will supposedly rejuvenate, renew, refresh or regenerate the skin. As a cream or ointment, it is used to heal burns and other wounds.

If you are healthy, there is still a place for royal jelly in your life. It will supposedly make you better at sports, improve your memory and ability to learn and, as a bonus, improve your self-confidence.

It's available in many forms — added to drinks or yoghurt, refrigerated or frozen, as a paste or pills. It's more commonly sold as a 1–3% mixture with honey, or freeze-dried.

The list of celebrities whom it is claimed take royal jelly is extensive. It includes Hollywood stars, royal families from around the globe, politicians and world leaders, sports stars and super models. The list even covers more than just the human race. No, royal jelly has not been credited with giving the UFO Space People their superior skills. But the prize show winning abilities of greyhounds, racehorses, homing pigeons and even cats have been attributed to it.

And the unbelievable logic behind the outrageous claims is always the same. Surely, if royal jelly can turn an ordinary bee into a queen bee, it has to be able to do something equally wonderful for you.

The Scientific Claims

The 'scientific' claims are usually blessed with meaningless pseudo-scientific gibberish. For example, 'it is an adaptogen, a food that helps the body to help itself, and creates a balance'.

Royal jelly is claimed to have all the amino acids that we need in our diet. That is absolutely true — but then, so do meat and soya beans.

It is also claimed that royal jelly is very rich in vitamins. Unfortunately, this is blatantly incorrect. Royal jelly has hardly any vitamin C, and even less (if any at all) of vitamins A, D and K — though it does have some rather strange fatty acids. It was originally thought that there would be lots of vitamin E in royal jelly, thanks to the enormous fertility of the queen bee. But no, there is virtually none.

However, there are moderate amounts of the B vitamins in royal jelly.

Again, due to the fertility of the queen bee, it was claimed that royal jelly was rich in sex hormones. This claim was made totally without the benefit of taking any actual measurements. Royal jelly has only microscopic levels of any sex hormones. Recently, the male sex hormone, testosterone, has been identified, but only by using extremely sensitive techniques. The amount of testosterone in one gram of royal jelly is about 250,000 to 1,000,000 times less than the average adult human male produces in one day.

Royal jelly is supposed to lower cholesterol levels. But while this has often been claimed, it has never been proven.

It is true that it has some antibiotic properties. However, it covers only a small range of bacteria, and is only about one-quarter as powerful as the original penicillin. Antibiotics have come a long way since then. But in an emergency, royal jelly would be better than nothing.

The Side Effects

Paracelsus (1493–1541) was one of the first scientific doctors and pharmacologists. He recognised that all drugs have side effects, and said something to the effect that 'all drugs are poisons, what matters is the dose'.

Bee Genders

Bees seem to have three genders.

First, there is the single queen. She is definitely female. She takes 16 days to grow from egg to adult, and will live for some six years.

Second, there are the worker bees, up to 60,000 of them in each beehive. They are female, but usually have no functioning ovaries, so they don't normally produce eggs. They take 21 days to grow from an egg to an adult. Their life span is some 42 active days. So if they are hatched just before winter, they will be quite inactive during the winter, and can live for several months. But in those several months, they will have only some 42 days in which they are fully active. They come from eggs that the queen bee has fertilised with her stored sperm. Both the queen bee, and all the female worker bees, have genes from both the queen bee's mother and father.

Third, there are drones, up to a few thousand in number in each beehive. They are male. They take 24 days to grow from an egg to an adult. Their only job is to fertilise the queen bee. They arrive in the spring, and after mating with the queen bee, the survivors are booted out from the hive in the autumn and die. They can live for up to six months. They come from eggs that have not been fertilised with sperm. So they have genes only from the queen bee.

For absolutely no good reason, many of the adherents or devotees of royal jelly claim that because it is 'natural', it has no bad effects at all. Funnel web spider venom and fierce snake venom are each 100% natural, but they definitely have bad effects on people.

In the case of royal jelly, people who are asthmatics, or who are allergic to bee stings, are definitely at a high risk of serious side effects. These can range from the mild (skin irritations) to serious (bronchial distress) to deadly (anaphylactic shock).

It causes allergic contact dermatitis in 20% of those into whom it's injected. (In its early days, royal jelly was often injected, usually into the muscle or into the abdominal peritoneum.)

Royal Jelly — 1

The first thing to realise is that royal jelly is not a single substance. It is a mixture.

The nursing bees feed the larvae directly from their mouths. They have two main glands for this. The hypopharyngeal gland produces a clear liquid. This seems to be 'regular' food, full of nutrients. The mandibular gland produces a white liquid. This white liquid seems to carry both nutrients and the special chemicals that force the transformation. It seems to somehow force the ovaries to 'appear' or grow in the queen bee. These two liquids are not stored. They are disgorged and immediately exuded into the cells into which the eggs have been previously squirted by the queen bee.

In their early days, the larvae float in their individual cells, like balls in a sea of royal jelly. These cells have six sides, and are made from wax exuded from the bodies of the worker bees. The queen bee will pump out 1,500–3,000 fertilised eggs in the beehive each day. These fertilised eggs all have the same DNA, and are

Buzzing with enthusiasm

A colony of honeybees functions with the elegance and efficiency of a single organism. But while it has just one queen bee, it also has up to 60,000 sexually immature females who are the worker bees, and up to 1,000 males, known as drones.

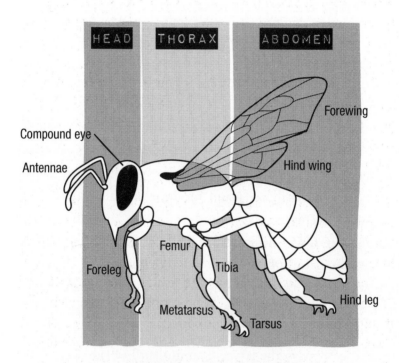

ANATOMY OF A BEE

essentially identical. All the bee eggs slosh around in royal jelly. The eggs take about three days to hatch into larvae.

The vast majority of the larvae start off getting a mixture of about 70% clear liquid (food) and 30% white liquid (food + 'special chemicals'). After a few days, this drops to 100% clear liquid and 0% white liquid. These larvae (destined to become workers) get just enough food to grow (known as 'progressive provisioning').

The Hive

A colony of honeybees functions with the elegance and efficiency of a single organism. But while it has just one queen bee, it also has up to 60,000 sexually immature females who are the worker bees, and up to 1,000 males, known as drones.

The honeybees do *not* collect honey from flowers – they make it. They collect pollen (equivalent to flowers' sperm) and transfer some of it to other flowers. But they keep most of it, because it contains proteins and fatty acids essential for the growth of young bees. They also collect nectar, a sugar solution in flowers that is some 50–80% water. They turn the nectar into honey, which is about 16–18% water. Over a calendar year, the hard-working bees may collect and bring back to the hive up to 450 kg of nectar, pollen and water.

The usual temperature inside the hive is about 34°C. The bees can use available water to cool down the hive if the external temperature stays below 49°C. They stop flying when the temperature falls below 14°C, and group themselves into a tight cluster to conserve heat. They can survive this way in temperatures as low as -46°C, but only for a few weeks.

However, the larvae destined to become queen bees get a different treatment. First, queen bee eggs are laid in extra-large cells (roughly the size, shape and texture of a peanut shell). Second, they are given more than they could ever possibly eat (known as 'mass provisioning'). Third, they are fed a 50:50 mixture of the clear and white liquids. This is what is called 'royal jelly'.

But three or four days after hatching from the eggs, the larvae that are destined to become worker bees have their royal jelly diluted with honey and pollen.

All the eggs have the potential to be a queen — but this metamorphosis happens only to the larvae fed on 100% royal jelly. If the hive becomes too populous, the worker bees select a dozen or so larvae to become potential queen bees. The chosen larvae undergo a complex series of hormonal and biochemical actions and reactions, as part of the process of turning into queen bees. After Day 5, they are ready to pupate, to turn from a larva into a bee.

Royal Jelly — 2

The only time royal jelly can be harvested is when too much of it is made. This happens during swarming, or queen replacement. During the subsequent 'queen rearing', the larvae destined to be queens are given too much to eat. This usually happens around Days 4 to 5 of the larvae's life. So all commercial royal jelly is the food originally intended for young queen bee larvae.

Typically, some 500 g of royal jelly can be produced from a well-managed hive during a season of some 5–6 months.

Royal jelly is similar in appearance, consistency and colour to condensed milk or mayonnaise. It has a cheese-like smell, and a characteristic sour flavour. (The unpleasant taste apparently makes it more acceptable as a 'medicine'.) It's whitish in colour, with beige or yellow tinges. It's about 60–70% water, with various proteins making up about 17–45% of its dry weight. Sugars (mostly sucrose and fructose) make up 18–52% of the dry weight. The rather odd fats account for 3.5–19% of the dry weight. Minerals constitute only 2–3% of the dry weight. They are, in descending order, potassium, calcium, sodium, zinc, copper and manganese.

It's about 10% more dense than water, and will dissolve slightly in water.

It is fairly viscous, having a consistency similar to warmish honey.

Royal jelly is essential in the diet of all worker bees for the first few days of their lives, and for the entire life of a queen bee.

Rather Odd Fats

The rather odd fats in royal jelly account for 3.5–19% of its dry weight.

There's something strange about those fats. To quote the United Nations report, 'The lipid fraction consists to 80–90% (by dry weight) of free fatty acids with unusual and uncommon structures. They are mostly short chain (8 to 10 carbon atoms) hydroxy fatty acids or dicarboxylic acids, in contrast to the fatty acids with 14 to 20 carbon atoms which are commonly found in animal and plant material. These fatty acids are responsible for most of the recorded biological properties of royal jelly. The principal acid is 10-hydroxy-2-decanoic acid, followed by its saturated equivalent, l0-hydroxydecanoic acid. In addition to the free fatty acids, the lipid fraction contains some neutral lipids, sterols (including cholesterol) and an unsaponifiable fraction of hydrocarbons similar to beeswax extracts.'

Young Queen

Before the potential queen bees emerge from their cells, the existing queen bee will suddenly leave the hive, taking a swarm of some 5,000–25,000 bees with her. After flying for a few minutes, the queen bee lands. She waits, surrounded by most of the swarm, while a few bees continue to fly, looking for a suitable home.

Back in the now depopulated and temporarily queen-less hive, one new queen emerges from her cell before the other potential queens. With a complete lack of either royal or female solidarity, she will try to murder the other queens still in their cells — but often the worker bees will try to stop her. However, if another queen bee emerges at the same time, they will fight until the death.

After a whole week of life as the new queen, it's time for what will be her one-and-only period of sexual mating. The drones (male honeybees) die in the act of mating. She will usually mate with up to ten drones per flight outside of the beehive, and she could have one flight each day over the next few days. (The giant Asian honeybee, *Apis dosata*, has been counted as having over 100 mates.) She will stop when she has enough sperm to fertilise each of the several thousand eggs that she will lay each day of the remaining three to five years of her long life (worker bees live for just five to six weeks during the active season). She will probably never leave the hive again, unless it becomes too populous, and in that case she flies off with a swarm accompanying her.

The future queen bee continues to be fed only royal jelly. She lives on the glandular secretions of the workers for the rest of her life. She never feeds herself.

She will be very different from the workers. She will be fertile, not sterile like the workers. She develops reproductive organs right from the beginning. But over their short lives, the worker

GOd sAVe the QUeen ... Bee

Despite her name, the queen bee doesn't run the hive –
she is its reproductive slave, and is the mother
of all the bees in the hive.

Royal jelly is an amazing piece of work. Its properties can change
regular baby bees (larvae) that are otherwise destined to
become worker bees, into queen bees.
Compared to the worker bees, a queen is
spectacularly fertile and long-lived.

bees successively activate 'organs related to [their] work such as pollen baskets, stronger mandibles, brood food glands and wax glands'. The queen bee will lay thousands of eggs each day, while the worker bees will lay an egg only very occasionally (perhaps one in 10,000 workers). The workers will, as the name implies, do all the work in the hive.

The queen bee develops more quickly than the worker bees. She is also much larger — up to three times the size.

The Life of a Worker Bee

The worker bees perform many different tasks once they have become an adult.

They clean the hive from Days 1–3. From Days 3–6 they feed the older larvae, and then graduate to feeding the younger larvae on Days 6–10. Then their food-producing glands begin to atrophy, and there is some overlap of various jobs. Days 8–16 can be spent accepting nectar and pollen from the foragers. They can become foragers themselves from Day 14, or they can guard the hive. They can make wax and build the comb cells from Days 12–18. The bees exude wax from special segments on their abdomens.

And it's all over around Day 42.

History of Unbelievable Claims

The spectacular biological transformation of a larva into a queen bee provided the background to the claims that royal jelly is a miracle therapy for human beings. These claims appeared in the French beekeeping press of the 1950s, and continually referred to 'research' carried out in various hospitals. However, the vast bulk of this so-called research could never be found in either the medical or scientific literature — only in the French beekeeping press.

The original claim for royal jelly's power was made around the time when the first antibiotic, penicillin, was performing truly marvellous cures. The royal jelly promotion got piggybacked onto the good press for penicillin. The very first claims for it were that it would 'rejuvenate' you. You were supposed to take 0.2–0.5 g each day, for a few months. You could swallow it, or let it melt under your tongue. Either way, it was supposed to act as a tonic and stimulant if you were unhealthy, or a euphoric if you were healthy.

But the truth is something very different.

It has never been proven that royal jelly does anything positive for us. There were a few Russian studies that looked at the claimed good effects of royal jelly on human beings in the 1950s and 1960s. But they all had flaws. None of the studies were well-designed — they lacked details on the exact test methods, lacked controls, were not double-blind, had very small sample sizes, tried to measure human attributes (e.g. rejuvenation, wellbeing and euphoria) that are impossible to measure, and so on.

So why did the public fall for the hype, and hand over their cash?

First, the queen bee's transformation is truly amazing. Second, the medical claims were amazing (but total fabrications). Third, there was a lot of advertising. And indeed, consumers wanted to believe that a simple outlay of cash would give them as dramatic a change as royal jelly did to a regular bee larva. Fourth, royal jelly was so rare, mysterious and exotic that it was possible to believe anything that was said about it.

I must admit that when I was a hippie, I was lured by the attractive claims, and briefly dabbled with royal jelly. But I was discouraged by the cost — similar to caviar — and the overwhelming lack of results.

Genetics 101

Regardless of the hype about the effect of royal jelly on human beings, it does do wondrous things to bee larvae.

To understand what's going on, you need to know a little genetics. I'll start with the Old School Genetics.

There are about 100 trillion cells in our bodies. Practically all of them have all the DNA needed to make another 'us'. The only cells that don't are the red blood cells (with no DNA at all) and the sex cells (sperm in males, ova in females). The sex cells have half the DNA needed to make a human being. Then, when a man and a woman love each other very much in a very special way, the sperm and egg combine, making a fertilised egg. The fertilised egg now has all the DNA needed to make a human being.

There are several hundred different types of cells in a human being — lung, liver, brain, heart, nerve, etc. What they all have in common is that they have DNA. The DNA in each cell looks like a ladder. This DNA ladder-of-life has about three billion 'rungs'. One of the great discoveries of the 20th century was that any three of these 'rungs' has all the information needed to 'tell' the rest of the cell to 'get' an amino acid. If you put a few amino acids together, you get a protein. For example, the protein 'insulin' has about 1,000 amino acids. The section of the DNA which 'made' the insulin was called the 'gene' for insulin.

If you assemble enough proteins together, you get a human being.

So the Old School Genetics thought that the DNA would control the RNA — which in turn would control the manufacture of proteins, which made cells, and ultimately, our bodies. It used to be thought that this was a one-way flow of information, from the DNA to the RNA to the proteins. The DNA was thought of as an 'architect's plan', which was simply read to make proteins. And a 'gene' was simply a section of the DNA that did one specific job.

But more recently we have learnt that information can flow in both directions.

Genetics 202

Yes, information can flow back to the DNA — and this can alter the DNA, or at least alter how it is read. (This is what happens with the bee larvae and royal jelly.)

Under the Old School Genetics theories, there were a lot of unanswered questions. For example, if the DNA is the same in each cell, how then do some cells turn into liver cells, while others turn into kidney cells?

The answer is that the genes are controlled, or regulated. For example, the kidney is made of kidney cells. These kidney cells have (like all the cells in the body) the potential to make any organ. But most of that potential is switched off. Only the genes to make kidney cells are switched on in the cells of the kidney.

It's the same in the liver, and the heart, and so on. Only the genes to make that particular organ are switched on, while all the others are switched off.

This process of making a kidney cell can be controlled at many different 'levels'. This control is called 'Gene Regulation'. The control can happen in the gene in the DNA, or when the RNA is made, or when the RNA is exported from the centre of the cell to where the proteins are made, etc.

The DNA is the same in all of our cells. This process of Gene Regulation is how the same DNA makes very different cells. In other words, the DNA is the same in every cell. But the process of what happens to the DNA, and how it is 'read' to make proteins, is very different in different cells.

If you haven't already guessed, Gene Regulation is a part of the New Genetics.

And this process of Gene Regulation is involved in how identical DNA in fertilised bee larvae can make very different creatures — a worker bee, or a queen bee.

At Last, Royal Jelly

So now we can understand what is happening with royal jelly. (Sorry that it took so long to get here, but this knowledge has taken the combined work of tens of thousands of scientists, spread over a period of a century and a half. It's a lot of knowledge.)

In 2008, Professor Ryszard Maleszka and his colleagues from the Australian National University lifted the lid on how royal jelly turns a regular egg into a queen bee.

Professor Maleszka showed that changing the methyl groups that were added to the DNA could start the process of turning what would be worker bees into queen bees.

The 'rungs' on the DNA are still unchanged. But chemical and possibly physical changes have been made to the DNA. This new branch of science is called epigenetics. The chemical change is that methyl groups (CH_3) have been added to the rungs. If the rungs are read by the various mechanisms in the cell, they will produce the same proteins. But the methyl groups stop the rungs from being read. (This chemical change is called 'methylation'.)

The physical change is related to how the DNA is packaged up. After all, this 'ladder' with three billion rungs is about 2–3 m long. It has to be all curled up very tightly so that it can fit into a cell only a few millionths of a metre across. The bits of the DNA that are at the very centre of the curled-up DNA can't be read — in the same way that the very inside of a tightly balled-up sock won't get washed in the washing machine. But the bits of the sock on the outside can get washed free of dirt — just like the bits on the outside of the curled-up ball of the DNA can be read. (This physical change is called 'chromatin remodelling'.)

So now we know that if you feed lots of royal jelly to a bee larva, methyl groups get added to the bee's DNA and it turns into a queen. (But we are still not sure exactly what chemicals in the royal jelly do this, or exactly which sections of the DNA they act on.)

It seems that royal jelly alters how the bee DNA is read. But, it works only on bee DNA, not on human DNA.

Prostate Cancer

Today we know that it's not just the DNA that you got from your parents that controls what happens to you — it's also your environment.

First, let's look at prostate cancer and the effect of a healthy lifestyle.

The prostate is a gland that in men is wrapped around the urethra. We used to think that only some men got cancer of the prostate. Today, we think that virtually all the men that reach their 80s will have some kind of prostate cancer. In the vast majority of cases, the cancer will not bother them, and will not shorten their lives.

One study showed that a healthy lifestyle could act on the DNA in the prostate cancer and trigger genetic changes. In other words, information could flow from outside the cell (good diet and exercise) and modify the DNA to slow down the prostate cancer.

This small study followed 30 men with low-risk prostate cancer. There was no need for them to have any medical treatment such as surgery, chemotherapy or radiotherapy.

These men then underwent major lifestyle changes. They started eating a diet rich in healthy foods, such as fruit, vegetables, legumes, soy products, whole grains, etc. They also started spending half an hour each day doing moderate exercise. And, finally, they spent as much as an hour each day on stress management methods such as meditation.

After three months, there were obvious changes. They lost weight, had lower blood pressure, felt better, had more energy, etc.

But the DNA in their prostate cancer had also been changed!

To get this information, they biopsied the prostate cancer both before and after the lifestyle change.

In their DNA, these men naturally had genes to fight the prostate cancer. Unfortunately, before the lifestyle change, these genes had been switched off. But now about 48 of these protector genes had been turned on, and were fighting the prostate cancer.

In their DNA, these men also naturally had genes that could help the prostate cancer grow. Unfortunately, before the lifestyle intervention, these genes had been switched on. But now about 453 of these genes were turned off, and were no longer helping the cancer grow.

In other words, the environment external to the prostate gland (what they ate, how they handled stress and their new exercise regime) changed how the DNA in their cancer was now being read.

Dutch Famine, 1944

So the bottom line of epigenetics is that information can flow back to the DNA, and change what it does.

Sometimes these changes to the DNA can last for generations.

In mid-1944, the Allies landed in Europe, to boot out the occupying Nazi forces. In Holland, the Allies started Operation Market Garden, to gain control of the bridge across the Rhine River at Arnhem. (This is the subject of the movie *A Bridge Too Far*.) The local Dutch also rose in rebellion against the Nazi rulers. But Operation Market Garden failed, and the Dutch were punished by having their food restricted.

The adult rations were dropped to as low as 580 calories per day (about one-quarter of the minimum daily requirement). Unfortunately, the winter of 1944–1945 was unusually harsh, making food demands higher than usual. It was later called 'The Dutch Famine of 1944' or the 'Hunger Winter'.

As you would expect, the pregnant women gave birth to smaller than normal children. But apparently there were epigenetic changes to the DNA of these wartime babies. When these girls grew up, and had babies themselves, their new babies were also smaller than normal, and so on to the next generation.

So the terrible famine experienced by the pregnant mothers made permanent changes to the DNA of their children. The 'rungs' of the DNA were still the same, but how the rungs were read and turned into proteins was changed.

Epigenetics — Twins

Identical twins can be very similar, or a little different.

They start off with identical DNA, when the fertilised egg splits into two. But from that moment on, they are treated differently. One might be fed more nutrients through a short and fat umbilical cord, while the other would get fewer nutrients through a long and thin umbilical cord.

There are cases where one twin is schizophrenic, while the other is not. Yep, it's probably epigenetics at work — the environment changing how the DNA is read.

One study looked at 40 pairs of identical twins from Spain, Denmark and the UK. Their ages ranged from 3 to 74 years, and 25 pairs were female.

The big surprise (at least, it would be a surprise if you didn't know about epigenetics, which has already told us why and how a combination of diet and exercise can alter the course of some cancers, or how your lifestyle can affect your DNA) was that the youngest twins had the most similar DNA. The older the twins were, the more likely that their DNA was different. And the more time the twins spent apart from each other and in different environments, the more their DNA was different.

These are still early days, but scientists think that foods, exposure to environmental chemicals and pollutants, levels of physical activity, and perhaps even powerful emotional experiences could affect how the DNA is read.

More Epigenetics

One study looked at male rats that were exposed to the crop fungicide vinclozolin while they were still in the uterus. Once they grew into adult rats, they were less fertile than unexposed rats. They also had more cancer and kidney problems. That was to be expected. What was unusual was that these problems were passed down the male line for three more generations. The 'rungs' in the rats' DNA were unchanged, but there were lots of methyl groups added to the DNA.

Another study looked at male mice that inhaled cocaine. As expected, they had memory problems. And yes, the baby mice also had memory problems. And again, the 'rungs' of the DNA were not changed, but methyl groups were added.

So Here's the Buzz

It would be fun if royal jelly could add some buzz to your day — but unless you're a bee, it won't.

So if you're seeking rejuvenation, why not follow the example of the worker bee and increase your exercise. It'll do more good for you than a jar of royal jelly (and without any sting) ...

Your Prostate

At one stage in my life, I found myself turning up at Long Bay Jail (in New South Wales) on a regular basis. No, it was not weekend detention. As a medical doctor, I was involved in teaching the prisoners some basic anatomy and physiology relating to sexual matters. I was at first a little taken aback at how little the guys knew. But then I remembered how little I knew about my own body before I studied medicine. So it wasn't a big surprise to read that the vast majority of Australian men did not know what the prostate gland did.

There are some very good reasons for men to understand the prostate gland – after all, it's somehow involved in sex, and apparently it can go wrong. And yet, according to a recent survey of 503 men aged 40–80 years in Western Australia, 80% of men did not know what the function of the prostate gland was. This was despite the fact that 75% of them had had a previous prostate-related examination, and that about 50% of them had experienced cancer of the prostate (either they had it, or a friend had it).

The prostate gland was first described in 1536, and its cancer first identified in 1853. In the USA and the UK, cancer of the prostate is the second most common cause of cancer deaths in men, after lung cancer. In Australian men, it's the second most common cancer after cancers of the skin, and, again, it's the number two cause of cancer deaths.

Most men with prostate cancer do not have any symptoms from it, and so do not get any treatment for it. Indeed, they end up dying from other causes. This is because cancer of the prostate can grow very slowly, and also because most men with cancer of the prostate are over 60 years of age. Indeed, in studies of men who died from other causes, autopsies show that cancer of the prostate was present in 30% of men in their 50s, and in 80% of men in their 70s.

The prostate gland is about 3 cm long, and weighs about 20 g. It is usually said to be the size of a walnut or a chestnut. It's located deep in the pelvis, directly under the urinary bladder, and immediately in front of the rectum. The urethra, after leaving the bladder on its way to the outside world, passes through the middle of the prostate gland. So as the prostate gland enlarges with age, it can have two effects. First, it can constrict or squash the urethra, so interfering with normal urination, and sexual ejaculation as well. Second, an enlarged prostate can bulge upwards into the bladder, so giving a false sense of bladder fullness.

The tissue of the prostate gland is about 5% non-glandular (with fibro-muscular components) and 95% glandular (from which cancers of the prostate arise). In the glandular part, there are some 30–50 little glands that secrete various fluids (collectively known as prostatic fluid) into pipes that eventually lead to the urethra. Prostatic fluid is a clear, slightly alkaline liquid with a rather characteristic smell. The alkalinity is thought to improve the survivability of the sperm in the vagina. Prostatic fluid makes up about 10–30% of the volume of the semen. About 10% of the volume of the semen comes from the vas deferens, and the remainder comes from the seminal vesicles. (By the way, semen has about 90 calories – 378 kj – of nutritional value.)

So the 95% of the prostate gland that is glandular makes prostatic fluid. But the 5% of the prostate gland that is fibro-muscular has another function – a muscular function. During ejaculation, it provides exquisitely timed waves of muscular contraction on the outside of the urethra to help propel semen to its final destination.

In the past, the prostate has not received a lot of attention in the media, but this situation has changed over the last decade. Messages about screening can be a bit confusing, but I guess that there's nothing wrong with knowing more about any part of your body. So, boys, take care – the prostate gland could cause you a wee problem . . .

References

Dennin, Carina, 'Epigenetics and disease: altered states', *Nature*, 13 February 2003, pp 686–688.

Encyclopaedia Britannica, 2008 Ultimate Reference Suite DVD — 'Beekeeping', 'Honeybee'.

Fraga, Mario F., et al., 'Epigenetic differences arise during the lifetime of monozygotic twins', *Proceedings of the National Academy of Science* (PNAS), 26 July 2005, Vol 102, No 30, pp 10604–10609.

Krell, R., *Value-Added Products from Beekeeping*, FAO Agricultural Service Bulletin No 124, Rome: Food and Agricultural Organization of the United Nations, 1996.

Kucharski, R., et al., 'Nutritional control of reproductive status in honeybees via DNA methylation', *Science*, 28 March 2008, Vol 319, No 5871, pp 1827–1830.

Lloyd, John and Mitchinson, John, *QI: The Book of Animal Ignorance*, London: Faber and Faber, 2007, pp 20–21.

Ornish, Dean, et al., 'Changes in prostate gene expression in men undergoing an intensive nutrition and lifestyle intervention', *Proceedings of the National Academy of Science* (PNAS), 17 June 2008, Vol 105, No 24, pp 8369–8374.

Young, Emma, 'Strange inheritance: it's not just your parents' genes but also their experiences that determine your genetic make-up', *New Scientist*, 12 July 2008, pp 29–33.

AcknowLedGements

This book could not have been written without the hard work of (literally) millions of scientists around the world who do the original research, as well as the scientific journals that publish their research.

Several Real Scientists checked some of the stories — they include Dr David Fink, Professor Ron Trent, Professor Gareth Denyer, Professor Jennie Brand-Miller, Professor Benjamin Oldroyd, Josh Dowling, Dr David Pyne, Dr Helen O'Connor and Professor Louise Bourke.

On the HarperCollins side, Lydia Papandrea and Janice Godwin edited my very late manuscript (but I did have 10 weeks holiday in less than a year), Shona Martyn and Amruta Slee were my wonderful publishers, Nicola Howcroft, Marie Slocombe and Christine Farmer worked very cleverly to make the general public aware of this slim volume, while Sophie Hamley most competently agented on my behalf. Dan Driscoll at the ABC in Sydney added his clever and irreverent puns, and reshaped the stories at an early stage in their lives. And Caroline Pegram did most of the above, as well as designing the concept for the cover.

Adam Yazxhi inked (on a computer) all the illustrations and the cover, and did the difficult (but very worthy) pics for 'How to Measure the Distance to the Moon with a Coin'. The punk-inspired clothing (on the lovely cover) was supplied by Adam Ventress.

And bearing in mind that without Family and Friends one is a Rudderless Ship, Big It Up for My Family: Mary, Little Karl (who is now taller at just under two metres), Alice and Lola all provided the seeds of ideas for the stories; Mary also did the necessary (but brutal, yet essential) preliminary editing and structural re-arrangement and additions necessary to make these stories live; and Carmel and Max patiently and proficiently pored over the page proofs.

Finally, I would like to thank the individual stories themselves. Some of them were happy at around 1,000 words, while others just grew and grew until they were happy. But they all taught me something – and now I know How To Measure the Distance to the Moon with a Coin.

Other Dr Karl titles

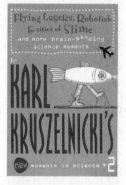

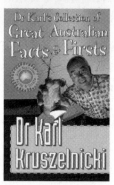

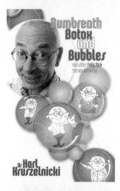